Houghton Mifflin Reading

Practice Book

Level 3.1

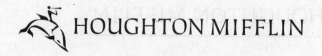

HOUGHTON MIFFLIN

Practice Book

Illustration:
Ruth Flanigan 3, 5-15, 17-22, 152; Robert Byrd 23, 25-37, 120; Hilarie Holdsworth 38, 40, 41, 43-52; Anna Dewdney 56, 57, 187-191, 193-196, 198, 199; Terry Weidner 61-64, 66-75, 77-80; Dan Brawner 81-89, 91, 93, 95; Gloria Calderon 96, 98-104, 106-110; Brian Lies 113-119, 121-123, 125, 136-149, 151; Judy Love 130, 131, 133, 153, 154-156, 172-178, 180-184, 186, 206, 207; Francisco Mora 157-169, 171. Notebooks and paper by Nathan Jarvis.

Photography:
Photographs by Ralph J. Brunke Photography.

HOUGHTON MIFFLIN

Contents

Contents

Name _____

Strategy Workshop

As you listen to the story "The Rule," by Anne Cameron, you will stop from time to time to do some activities on these practice pages. These activities will help you think about different strategies that can help you read better. After completing each activity, you will discuss what you've written with your classmates and talk about how to use these strategies.

Remember, strategies can help you become a better reader. Good readers

- use strategies whenever they read

- use different strategies before, during, and after reading

- think about how strategies will help them

Strategy I: Predict/Infer

Use this strategy before and during reading to help make predictions about what happens next or what you're going to learn.

Here's how to use the Predict/Infer strategy:
1. Think about the title, the illustrations, and what you have read so far.
2. Tell what you think will happen next—or what you will learn. Thinking about what you already know about the subject may help.
3. Try to figure out things the author does not say directly.

Listen as your teacher begins "The Rule." When your teacher stops, complete the activity with a partner to show that you understand how to predict what you think might happen in the story.

Think about the story and respond to the question below.

What do you think might happen in the story?

_____

_____

As you continue listening to the story, think about whether your prediction was right. You might want to change your prediction or write a new one below.

_____

_____

_____

Name _____

Strategy 2: Phonics/Decoding

Use this strategy during reading when you come across a word you don't know.

Here's how to use the Phonics/Decoding strategy:

1. Look carefully at the word.
2. Look for word parts that you know and think about the sounds for the letters.
3. Blend the sounds to read the word.
4. Ask yourself if this is a word you know and whether the word makes sense in the sentence.
5. If not, ask yourself if there is anything else you could try—should you look in the dictionary?

Listen as your teacher continues to read the story. When your teacher stops, use the Phonics/Decoding strategy.

Now write down the steps you used to decode the word *trout*.

_____

_____

_____

_____

_____

_____

Remember to use this strategy whenever you are reading and come across a word that you don't know.

Name _____

Strategy 3: Monitor/Clarify

Use this strategy during reading whenever you're confused about what you are reading.

Here's how to use the Monitor/Clarify strategy:

- Ask yourself if what you're reading makes sense—or if you are learning what you need to learn.
- If you don't understand something, reread, look at the illustrations, or read ahead to see if that helps.

Listen as your teacher continues to read the story. When your teacher stops, complete the activity with a partner to show that you understand how to figure out why the boy in the story might think the mushrooms look like a forest.

Think about the story and respond below.

1. Have you ever eaten mushrooms? What do they look like?

   _____

   _____

2. Can you tell from listening to the story why the boy may have thought the mushrooms looked like a forest? Why or why not?

   _____

   _____

3. How can you find out why he may have thought that?

   _____

   _____

Name _____

Strategy 4: Question

Use this strategy during and after reading to ask questions about important ideas in the story.

Here's how to use the Question strategy:

- Ask yourself questions about important ideas in the story.
- Ask yourself if you can answer these questions.
- If you can't answer the questions, reread and look for answers in the text. Thinking about what you already know and what you've read in the story may help you.

Listen as your teacher continues to read the story. Then complete the activity with a partner to show that you understand how to ask yourself questions about important ideas in the story.

Think about the story and respond below.

Write a question you might ask yourself at this point in the story.

_____

_____

_____

_____

_____

If you can't answer your question now, think about it while you listen to the rest of the story.

Name _____

Strategy 5: Evaluate

Use this strategy during and after reading to help you form an opinion about what you read.

Here's how to use the Evaluate strategy:
- Think about how the author makes the story come alive and makes you want to read it.
- Think about what was entertaining, informative, or useful about the selection.
- Think about how you reacted to the story—how well you understood the selection and whether you enjoyed reading it.

Listen as your teacher continues to read the story. When your teacher stops, complete the activity with a partner to show that you are thinking of how you feel about what you are reading and why you feel that way.

Think about the story and respond below.

1. Tell whether or not you think this story is entertaining and why.

_____

_____

2. This is a humorous, realistic fiction story. Did the author make the characters interesting and believable?

_____

_____

3. How did you react to this story?

_____

Name _____

Strategy 6: Summarize

Use this strategy after reading to summarize what you read.

Here's how to use the Summarize strategy:
- Think about the characters.
- Think about where the story takes place.
- Think about the problem in the story and how the characters solve it.
- Think about what happens in the beginning, middle, and end of the story.

Think about the story you just listened to. Complete the activity with a partner to show that you understand how to identify important story parts that will help you summarize the story.

Think about the story and respond to the questions below:

1. Who is the main character?

_____

_____

2. Where does the story take place?

_____

_____

3. What is the problem and how is it resolved?

_____

_____

Now use this information to summarize the story for a partner.

Name _____

Off to Adventure!

Cut out a picture of something you think is an adventure from a magazine or a newspaper. Paste it on this page. Then answer the questions below.

I. What do you think makes this an adventure?

_____

_____

2. How would you describe this adventure to someone?

_____

_____

3. Would you like to be part of this adventure? Explain your answer.

_____

_____

Name _____

Off to Adventure!

As you read each selection in *Off to Adventure!*, fill in the boxes of the chart that apply to the selection.

	How does the adventure begin?	How do the characters change by the end of the adventure?
The Lost and Found		
The Ballad of Mulan		
The Waterfall		

Name _____

What a Day!

Joey has just moved to a new town. Help him finish a letter to his friend. Fill in the blanks with the correct words from the box.

September 5

Dear Flora:

My first day of school was full of unlucky

_____situations_____. I wanted to wear my favorite

shirt, but it was all _____rumpled_____ from being

packed in a box. While I was looking for something else to

wear, I missed the bus. My parents drove me to school, but we

got lost on the way. We had to stop and ask for

_____directions_____. I was _____worried_____

that I would be late for school, but we got there just in time.

At noon, I couldn't find my lunchbox. I looked everywhere,

but it wasn't _____visible_____. Then my day got

better. Some nice students asked me to sit with them. They

shared their lunches with me. It was an _____unusual_____

way to make new friends, but I'm glad it happened!

Your friend,

Joey

Theme 1: **Off to Adventure!**   3

Name _____

Event Map

Pages 20–21

Wendell and Floyd are at the principal's office. Then Mona
enters and says _she wants to find the_
lost and found to look for her lucky hat.

Pages 23

Mona leans so far into the bin that only her feet are showing.
A moment later, _she was gone!_

Pages 26–27

The boys _climbed into the lost and found bin to look_
for her.

Pages 30–31

The children see a sign to the Hat Room, so they follow a
passageway to _a cave, a lake, a suit of armour and a boat_

Pages 34–37

The children come to a hallway lined with doors. Finally, Mona
opens one last door and finds _the Hat room_

Name _____

Tell the True Story

**The underlined part of each sentence below is false.
Rewrite it as a true sentence about *The Lost and Found*.**

1. Wendell and Floyd are waiting to see the principal
   because <u>they missed their bus</u>.

   _____

   _____

2. Mona walks into the office <u>to borrow some lunch money</u>.

   _____

   _____

3. The boys want to climb into the Lost and Found bin <u>to
   get away from a giant squid</u>.

   _____

   _____

4. The children cross the lake to find <u>the school library</u>.

   _____

   _____

5. In the Hat Room, the boys start <u>looking for their lost
   baseball caps</u>.

   _____

   _____

6. Mona finds her lucky hat <u>hanging on the Hat Room door</u>.

   _____

   _____

Name _____

Story Events

Read the story. Think about what happens. Then fill in the chart on the next page.

Surprise!

After a long drive, Mom, Dad, and I got to Golden Lake. We were tired, so we set up camp and climbed into our sleeping bags. Then I said, "I hate camping. Why did you make me come?"

"You never know what can happen, Jenny," Dad answered. "You could be in for a big surprise!"

The next morning, I couldn't believe my eyes. There, sitting by the tent was a bee the size of an airplane! "Hop on!" shouted Dad over its loud hum. "Come for a ride."

We all got onto the bee's big, fuzzy back. Then it lifted off. It zoomed right and left. It sailed over the water and made loops in the air. What a fun ride!

At last, the bee landed by our camp. We all climbed off. Then it flew away. I stood there with my mouth open. Dad smiled and said, "Just wait until tomorrow's surprise!"

Name _____

Story Events continued

Finish each of the sentences to tell what happened in the story.

The family sets up camp at Golden Lake.

Jenny says she hates camping, but Dad tells her she may be in for a surprise.

The next morning _____

The family climbs onto its back.

Then the bee _____

At last the bee _____

The family climbs off.

The bee _____

Name _____

Base Words

Some words are formed from a **base word,** a word that can stand by itself. In the word *climbing*, the base word is *climb*. Letters can be added to the beginning or the end of a base word, as you see here.

appear/**dis**appear   boat/boat**er**   turn/turn**ed**

Some of the words in this Lost and Found bin contain base words. Circle the base word in those words. Then write each base word on the lines below.

asked   unusual   closer   only

principal   trying   nonsense   loosely

1. __ __ __
         4

2. __ __ __
         5

3. __ __
      2

4. __ __ __ __
         3

5. __ __ __ __

6. __ __ __ __ __ __
            1

How did the children feel at the end of the story?

Write the numbered letters in order from 1–5 to find out.

__ __ __ __ __
1 2 3 4 5

Name _____

Short Vowels

▶ A short vowel sound is usually spelled with one vowel followed by a consonant sound.

  The /ă/ sound is usually spelled **a,** as in l**a**st.

  The /ĕ/ sound is usually spelled **e,** as in sm**e**ll.

  The /ĭ/ sound is usually spelled **i,** as in m**i**x.

▶ Sometimes the /ĕ/ sound is spelled in a different way. In the starred words *head* and *friend*, the /ĕ/ sound is spelled *ea* and *ie*.

Write each Spelling Word under its vowel sound.

Spelling Words

1. mix
2. milk
3. smell
4. last
5. head*
6. friend*
7. class
8. left
9. thick
10. send
11. thin
12. stick

/ă/ Sound

_____

_____

/ĭ/ Sound

_____

_____

/ĕ/ Sound

_____

_____

_____

_____

Name _____

Spelling Spree

Silly Rhymes Write a Spelling Word to complete each silly sentence. Each answer rhymes with the underlined word.

1. Will chewing gum _____ to a <u>brick</u>?
2. Don't pile <u>bread</u> on your _____!
3. Never drink _____ while wearing <u>silk</u>.
4. You have to be _____ to squeeze under a <u>bin</u>.
5. <u>Fix</u> the ladder and _____ the batter.
6. How can you <u>tell</u> if bees can _____?

1. _____
2. _____
3. _____
4. _____
5. _____
6. _____

Letter Math Write a Spelling Word by adding and taking away letters from the words below.

Example: d + fish - f = *dish*

7. spend - p   = _____

8. c + glass - g   = _____

9. leg - g + ft   = _____

10. fri + mend - m = _____

11. blast - b   = _____

12. th + sick - s   = _____

Name _____

Proofreading and Writing

Proofreading Circle the five misspelled Spelling Words in the sign. Then write each word correctly.

MY LUCKY HAT IS LOST!

Please help me find my lucky hat. I don't know where I leaft it. The hat is green and has a thine blue ribbon. It is soft and kind of rumpled. The last time I had it was before clas on Monday. If you find it, please stik a note on my locker.

Your freind and classmate,
Mona

Spelling Words

1. mix
2. milk
3. smell
4. last
5. head*
6. friend*
7. class
8. left
9. thick
10. send
11. thin
12. stick

1. _____

2. _____

3. _____

4. _____

5. _____

Write a Description Have you ever lost something that you liked very much, such as a piece of clothing or a toy?

On a separate sheet of paper, write a short description of the item you lost. Make sure to include details that would help someone recognize it. Use Spelling Words from the list.

Name _____

Find the Right Order

The words in the Lost Bin have simply been tossed in any old order. Put the words in alphabetical order and write them in the Found Bin.

LOST BIN

muddle	principal
paddle	suggest
squeeze	crazy
plunge	mutter
middle	groan

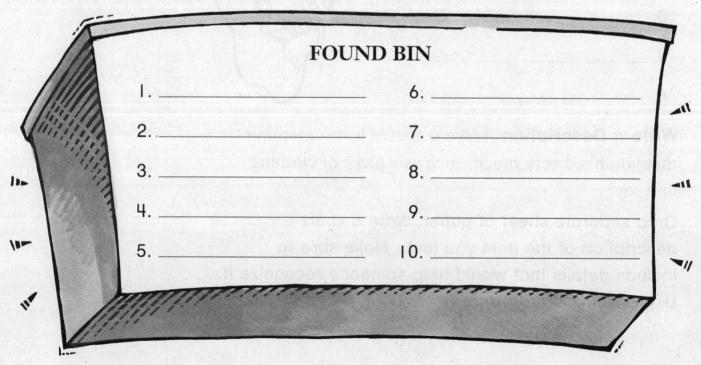

FOUND BIN

1. _____   6. _____

2. _____   7. _____

3. _____   8. _____

4. _____   9. _____

5. _____   10. _____

Name _____

Finding Sentences

Read each group of words. Write *sentence* if the words are a complete sentence. Write *fragment* if the words are not a complete sentence. Then rewrite each fragment as a complete sentence. Add a word or words from the box at the bottom of the page.

1. Floyd wanted a hat. _____

   _____

2. Examined a suit of armor. _____

   _____

3. The rumpled lucky hat. _____

   _____

4. Mona looked for her missing hat. _____

   _____

5. Floated on the water. _____

   _____

6. Flipped a coin. _____

   _____

Word Bank		
adventures	disappeared	Floyd
Mona	the boat	Wendell
worked		

Name _____

Changing Fragments to Sentences

Use each fragment below in a complete sentence.

1. Floyd and his friend Wendell

   _____

2. into a lost and found box

   _____

3. loses her lucky hat

   _____

4. looks like a dragon

   _____

5. in the hat room

   _____

6. an exciting adventure in a strange world

   _____

7. decides which cave to explore

   _____

8. a burgundy fez with a small gold tassel

   _____

Name _____

Finding Sentences

Effective writers use complete sentences. Correct each sentence fragment. Write your revised sentence on each line. If it is a complete sentence, write the word *correct*.

Lucky Hats for Lucky Cats

1. Mona's cat. Likes Mona's lucky hat.

   _____

2. Laughs at the ridiculous cat.

   _____

3. The playful cat. Bites the floppy hat.

   _____

4. Then the cat runs away with the hat.

   _____

5. Chases her cat into the basement.

   _____

6. She hears. A meow.

   _____

7. Mona opens the suitcase.

   _____

8. The cat. Is on her lucky hat.

   _____

Name _____

Planning the Body of a Friendly Letter

Think about an experience you will share in your friendly letter. Use the chart to plan a paragraph about it. Remember to include details that will interest your audience (the person who will read your letter).

Topic Sentence:

_____

_____

Supporting Detail

_____

_____

Supporting Detail

_____

_____

Supporting Detail

_____

_____

Name _____

Using Commas in Dates and Places

▶ When writing dates, use a comma between
the day and the year.   **Example:** May 12, 2003

▶ Use a comma after the year except at the end of a sentence.

Example: On June 30, 2003, my sister will be ten years old.

▶ Use a comma between a town or city and the state.

Example: New Orleans, Louisiana

▶ Use a comma after the state except at the end of a sentence.

Example: My brother goes to college in New Orleans,
Louisiana, and we will visit him next month.

Proofread the letter and add commas where necessary.

653 Cauterskill Road
Catskills New York 12414
February 25 2005

Dear Uncle Frank,

　　Our class is taking a field trip to New York City. Mom
and Dad are going to be parent helpers. We want to
spend an evening with you. We take a bus to New York
New York on May 12 2005 and return on the morning of
May 14 2005. Can you let us know right away which date
is best for you?

Your nephew,
Michael

Evaluating Your Personal Narrative

Reread your story. What do you need to make it better? Use this page to help you decide. Put a checkmark in the box for each sentence that describes your personal narrative.

Rings the Bell!

- [ ] The beginning catches the reader's interest.
- [ ] The story is told in sequence and is easy to follow.
- [ ] Everything in my story is important to the topic.
- [ ] The sentences flow smoothly and don't repeat unnecessary information.
- [ ] There are almost no mistakes.

Getting Stronger

- [ ] The beginning could be more interesting.
- [ ] The sequence of events isn't always clear.
- [ ] There are some things that don't relate to the topic.
- [ ] I could combine some sentences to make this flow better.
- [ ] There are a few mistakes.

Try Harder

- [ ] The beginning is boring.
- [ ] Events are out of order and confusing to the reader.
- [ ] The story doesn't relate to the main topic.
- [ ] There are a lot of mistakes.

Name _____

Combining Sentences

**Combine each pair of sentences into one. Include all the
important parts of both sentences. Avoid repeating words.**

1. The water was cold. The water was full of sharks.

   _____

   _____

2. Nina dove in the water. Brenda dove in the water.

   _____

   _____

3. Paul screamed. Winston screamed.

   _____

   _____

4. Nina laughed. Nina shouted, "Come on in, fellas!"

   _____

   _____

5. Paul said, "No way!" Winston said, "No way!"

   _____

   _____

6. Brenda yelled, "These sharks are only toys!" Nina yelled,
   "These sharks are only toys!"

   _____

   _____

Name _____

Spelling Words

Look for spelling patterns you have learned to help you remember the Spelling Words on this page. Think about the parts that you find hard to spell.

Write the missing letters and apostrophe in the Spelling Words below.

1. hav _____

2. hav _____ _____ _____ _____

3. f _____ _____ nd

4. ar _____ _____ nd

5. _____ ne

6. th _____ n

7. th _____ n

8. th _____ m

9. befo _____ _____

10. bec _____ _____ _____ e

11. _____ ther

12. _____ _____ ther

Study List On another sheet of paper, write each Spelling Word. Check the list to be sure you spell each word correctly.

Spelling Words

1. have
2. haven't
3. found
4. around
5. one
6. than
7. then
8. them
9. before
10. because
11. other
12. mother

Spelling Spree

Sentence Fillers Write the Spelling Word from the list on this page that best completes each sentence.

1-2. "Scott, _____ you seen my coat?"

"No, I _____."

3. We drove _____ the block three times.

4. Our neighbors asked us to lend _____ our lawnmower.

5. For a while it was noisy, but _____ it got quiet.

6. We met at the theater _____ the movie started.

7. I don't want this one, I want the _____ one.

8. Tania _____ a five-dollar bill lying on the ground.

1. have
2. haven't
3. found
4. around
5. one
6. than
7. then
8. them
9. before
10. because
11. other
12. mother

1. _____
2. _____
3. _____
4. _____
5. _____
6. _____
7. _____
8. _____

Word Clues Write the Spelling Word that fits each clue best.

9. You can use this word when you give a reason.

10. This word isn't a father, but a _____.

11. This word is the first thing you say when you count.

12. You can use this word when you compare two things.

9. _____
10. _____
11. _____
12. _____

Name _____

Proofreading and Writing

Proofreading Circle the four misspelled Spelling Words in this postcard. Then write each word correctly on the lines below.

Spelling Words

1. have
2. haven't
3. found
4. around
5. one
6. than
7. then
8. them
9. before
10. because
11. other
12. mother

Dear Peter,

    I just wanted to send a card to say hi befor I get going again. I fond this one in a little store in Yellowknife. Things are going great, and I'll have a lot of stories to tell when I get home. I'm sorry I havn't written in so long. I'll try to be better about it than I have been. Say hi to Mom and Dad, and tell then I'll call soon.

      Love,
      Kim

1. _____ 3. _____

2. _____ 4. _____

Adventure Dialogue Get together with another student and write a dialogue about an adventure. Both people in the dialogue can be off adventuring, or you can have one of them stay at home. Use Spelling Words from the list.

22   Theme 1: **Off to Adventure!**

Name _____

Crossword Challenge!

Write the word that matches each clue in the puzzle.

Use the words in the box and your glossary for help.

Vocabulary

armor	comrades	endured	farewell
triumphant	troops	victorious	

Across

2. winning by defeating another

6. metal body covering

7. lasted through

Down

1. successful

3. companions

4. good-bye

5. soldiers

Unscramble the last word to complete the sentence.

The Ballad of Mulan is an old Chinese **(nedlge)**

_____ .

Name _____

Inference Chart

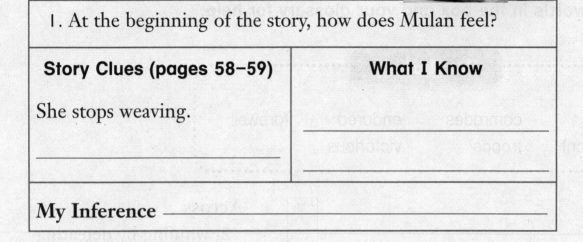

1. At the beginning of the story, how does Mulan feel?	
Story Clues (pages 58–59)	**What I Know**
She stops weaving. _____	_____ _____
My Inference _____	

2. Why does Mulan decide to help her father?	
Story Clues (pages 60–63)	**What I Know**
_____ _____	_____ _____
My Inference _____	

3. Years later, how does the Emperor feel about Mulan?	
Story Clues (pages 74–75)	**What I Know**
_____ _____	_____ _____
My Inference _____	

Name _____

Answers About Mulan

Answer these questions about *The Ballad of Mulan*.

1. Why does the Emperor need troops?

_____

_____

2. Why does Mulan go to war in her father's place?

_____

_____

3. After the war, why does the Emperor want to honor Mulan?

_____

_____

4. How does Mulan's family feel about having her come home?

_____

_____

5. When Mulan returns home, what does she choose to do?

_____

_____

6. What is the meaning of Mulan's statement about the rabbits?

_____

_____

7. Why do the Chinese still honor Mulan?

_____

_____

Name _____

Make a Good Guess

**Read the story below. Then answer the
questions on the following page.**

The Ice Girl

Trolls were raiding the valley. They swooped down
from icy mountain caves, looking for workers and burning
houses and barns. Those unlucky enough to be caught
never saw daylight again. The people in the valley called
a meeting to deal with the problem.

Greta sat and knitted. Ever since Father had
fallen, Brother was doing all the family chores. Even at
this late hour, he had gone to town while Father slept.
Greta helped as best she could. In her spare time, she
knitted and knitted. Perhaps her work would help to
keep them from selling a cow.

Suddenly, Greta heard a noise outside. Trolls!
She slipped out a side door and stood waiting. Sure
enough, four ugly trolls peered around the barn. Greta stood
still. Slowly the trolls crept closer and closer, but Greta never
moved. Finally she felt the steam from their mouths. Then
she gathered all her strength and yelled, "Boo!" as loud as she
could. The trolls jumped. Then they ran off, as fast as their
feet could move. From that day on, no troll ever came back to
the valley again.

And to this day, people remember her deed. They have
even put up a sign. It reads, "Here is where Greta, the Ice
Girl, once lived. She drove the trolls away by saying '*Boo!*'"

Name _____

Make a Good Guess continued

Use clues from the story and what you know to answer each question below.

1. What did the people want to do about the trolls?

   _____

   _____

2. What happened to people who were caught by the trolls?

   _____

   _____

3. Why did Brother have to do all the family chores?

   _____

   _____

4. Why did Greta spend so much time knitting?

   _____

   _____

5. At the end, why were no trolls ever seen in the valley again?

   _____

   _____

Name _____

Syllabication

If you come across a word you can't pronounce, try dividing the
word into **syllables**, or parts of a word that are said out loud
as single sounds. Each word below has two syllables.
Each can be divided in a different way.

Divide the compound word into two words:

sunrise = sun • rise

**Divide the word between
two consonants:**

village = vil • lage

**Write the words below with spaces between the two
syllables. Divide them either between the words in a
compound word or between two consonants.**

1. mirror   _____

   _____

2. nightfall   _____

   _____

3. poster   _____

   _____

4. mountain   _____

   _____

5. downtown   _____

   _____

Name _____

More Short Vowels

A short vowel sound is usually spelled with one vowel
followed by a consonant sound.

The /ŏ/ sound is usually spelled o, as in lot.

The /ŭ/ sound is usually spelled u, as in rub.

► Sometimes the /ŭ/ sound is spelled in a different way.
In the starred words *does* and *won*, the /ŭ/ sound is
spelled *oe* and *o*.

Write each Spelling Word under its vowel sound.

Spelling Words

1. pond
2. luck
3. drop
4. lot
5. rub
6. does*
7. drum
8. sock
9. hunt
10. crop
11. shut
12. won*

/ŏ/ Sound

_____

_____

_____

_____

/ŭ/ Sound

_____

_____

_____

_____

_____

_____

Theme 1: **Off to Adventure!**   29

Name _____

Spelling Spree

Finding Words **Write the Spelling Word hidden in each of these words.**

1. shutter _____

2. wonderful _____

3. plot _____

4. rubber _____

5. doesn't _____

6. eardrum _____

Spelling Words

1. pond
2. luck
3. drop
4. lot
5. rub
6. does*
7. drum
8. sock
9. hunt
10. crop
11. shut
12. won*

Questions **Write a Spelling Word to answer each question.**

7. What do you wear inside a shoe?

8. What does a farmer grow?

9. What can help you win a game?

10. What body of water is smaller than a lake?

11. What do lions do to get their dinner?

12. What do you call a tiny bead of water?

7. _____   10. _____

8. _____   11. _____

9. _____   12. _____

Name _____

Proofreading and Writing

Proofreading Circle the five misspelled Spelling Words below. Then write each word correctly.

Spelling Words

1. pond
2. luck
3. drop
4. lot
5. rub
6. does*
7. drum
8. sock
9. hunt
10. crop
11. shut
12. won*

The Emperor Praises Mulan

The Emperor welcomed General Mulan to the High Palace today. First, a soldier played a huge drume. Then the Emperor gave a speech. He told how Mulan was willing to droppe everything to join the army. He said the famous general did not win battles by luk, but by skill and bravery. Now, thanks to Mulan, the war is wone. No longer dose an invading army threaten China. The gates of the Great Wall are safely shut.

1. _____   4. _____

2. _____   5. _____

3. _____

Write a Story Long ago, in a land far away, a brave young girl named Mulan began a dangerous adventure. How would you begin an adventure story? What setting would you use? It could be a dark jungle or a distant planet, or it might be your own neighborhood.

On a separate sheet of paper, write the opening paragraph of an adventure story. Use Spelling Words from the list.

Name _____

Multiple Meaning Words

> **long** *adjective* **1.** Having great length: *a long river.*
> **2.** Lasting for a large amount of time: *a long movie.*
> **3.** Lasting a certain length: *The show was an hour long.*
> ♦ *adverb* Far away in the past: *The dinosaurs lived long ago.*
> ♦ *verb* To wish or want very much: *The children longed for an ice cream cone.*

For each of the following sentences, choose the correct definition of the underlined word. Write the definition on the line.

1. Long ago, a girl named Mulan went into battle.

   _____

2. A long line of soldiers crossed the mountain.

   _____

3. The town longed for peace to return.

   _____

4. It was a long way to the Yellow River.

   _____

5. Mulan longed to hear her mother's voice.

   _____

6. The war was ten years long.

   _____

Name _____

Classifying Sentences

Read and classify each sentence. Write *statement*, *question*, *command*, or *exclamation* on the line provided.

1. Why did Mulan fight in the army? _____

2. What an amazing girl she is! _____

3. Tell me what her journey was like. _____

4. She was surrounded by many dangers. _____

5. Mulan's family and friends were very proud of her.

   _____

6. There she goes now! _____

7. Watch the victory parade. _____

8. Can you see Mulan at the front of the troops?

   _____

9. The musicians sing a song about Mulan's

   adventures. _____

10. How beautiful the music sounds!

   _____

Name _____

Arranging Sentences

Arrange these sentences to create an interview with Mulan. Four of the sentences are questions and four are the answers to these questions. On the lines below, write each question followed by its answer. Add the correct end marks.

I dressed in armor	I was terrified at first
Were you afraid	Why did you join the army
My father was too ill to fight	Look at my face and see how
Are you glad to be home	happy I am
	What did you wear

1. **Q:** _____

   A: _____

2. **Q:** _____

   A: _____

3. **Q:** _____

   A: _____

4. **Q:** _____

   A: _____

Name _____

Capitalizing and Punctuating Sentences

Capital letters and punctuation help us to understand writing. Three students decided to act out a scene from *The Ballad of Mulan*. Here is the script they wrote for the scene. Check the capitalization and punctuation of each sentence. Then rewrite the script, using the correct capitalization and punctuation.

Soldier 1: Mulan, is that really you

1. _____

Soldier 2: how is this possible

2. _____

Soldier 1: are you really a girl

3. _____

Mulan: yes, I am you have not seen the real me

4. _____

Soldier 1: you are brave and amazing

5. _____

Soldier 2: what a remarkable girl you are

6. _____

Mulan: I had to save my father would you have let me fight if I had dressed as a woman

7. _____

_____

Theme 1: **Off to Adventure!**   35

Name _____

Response Journal

Plan a Response Journal What did you learn about Mulan in *The Ballad of Mulan*? Write a journal entry that describes at least one important thing you learned about her character. Include supporting details from the story to explain each of your main idea's.

Main Idea: Mulan is brave.

Detail: _____

Detail: _____

Detail: _____

Main Idea: _____

Detail: _____

Detail: _____

Detail: _____

Name _____

Capitalizing Days and Months

▶ Begin an entry in your journal with the day or date.

▶ Begin the name of the day of the week with a capital letter.

Monday   Tuesday   Wednesday   Thursday
Friday   Saturday   Sunday

▶ Begin the months of the year with capital letters.

April 12
November 24

Write each day or date correctly.

1. wednesday _____

2. friday, november 18 _____

3. saturday _____

4. monday, january 7 _____

5. thursday _____

6. tuesday, may 8 _____

7. sunday _____

Name _____

Adventure Advertisement

Help rewrite this ad to make it more exciting. Replace the words in parentheses with words from the box. Fill in the blanks with the correct words.

Visit Adventure _____ (Valley)! Ride a canoe through _____ (fast, tiny waterfalls in a river). Dock your canoe and cross the river by stepping on huge _____ (round rocks). Walk past Silver Waterfall, where the river looks like a boiling _____ (kettle). After you've _____ (searched out) a path, hike to the top of the waterfall. Be careful! To climb the _____ (very steep) rock walls, you'll have to find _____ (rock shelves) on the sides of the cliffs.

Answer the following question. (Hint: If you need help, look at pages 92–93 in your textbook.)

What is a waterfall?

_____

_____

Name _____

Cause and Effect Chart

Cause (Why does it happen?)	→	Effect (What happens?)
_____	→	They wade through the cold water.
_____	→	They hear a roaring sound.
A wild animal comes down to the creek to drink.	→	_____
The boy is happy when he reaches the top.	→	_____
"The Dancer" reminds the boy of the waterfall and the camping trip.	→	_____

Name _____

Finish the Story

Complete each of the sentences with details from
The Waterfall.

1. In July the boy and his family _____

_____

2. The family finds a waterfall that is higher _____

_____

3. When the sun gets hot, the family keeps cool by

_____

_____

4. The next day, the boy and his brother climb _____

_____

5. As his parents climb up the steep rocks, the boy feels

_____

_____

6. The boy wants to bring the driftwood home because

_____

_____

_____

Name _____

Causes and Effects

**Read the story. Think about what happens and why.
Then complete the chart on the next page.**

The Tornado

A rooster crowed, waking Lucy Sunders from a deep sleep.
She usually popped out of bed like buttons pop off a shirt, but
today she was tired. She had stayed up late last night reading.

Lucy looked out her window. The sky was a funny yellow-
gray, and there were no sounds. Then, across the fields, Lucy
saw a whirling dust cloud. It grew bigger and bigger. A
tornado was coming!

Lucy raced down the stairs, shouting, "Mama, Mama —
a tornado!"

Mrs. Sunders checked the sky. Then she grabbed the baby
from his swing. "Run! Run to the root cellar!" she shouted.

Lucy and her mother ran through the yard, and Lucy
pulled open the cellar door. She hurried down the steps. Her
mother locked the door and followed her into the darkness.

Quickly Mrs. Sunders lit the old lamp, and the light
glowed warmly. Lucy sighed. They were safe now.
Everything would be all right.

Theme 1: **Off to Adventure!**   41

Name _____

Causes and Effects continued

In each box, write a cause or an effect from the story.

Cause (Why does it happen?)	Effect (What happens?)
	The noise wakes Lucy up.
	Lucy races down the stairs.
	Her mother grabs the baby and shouts, "Run!"
Lucy, Mama, and the baby will be safe from the tornado in the root cellar.	
	The lamp glows warmly.
Lucy, her mother, and the baby are in the root cellar.	

Name _____

Add the Ending

▶ For words that end with a vowel and a single
consonant, double the consonant before adding
-ed or *-ing*.

grip + p + ed = gripped   swim + m + ing = swimming

**Read the clues for the puzzle. For each one, choose
a word from the box with the same meaning as the
word in dark type. Complete the puzzle by adding
-ed or *-ing* to the word from the box.**

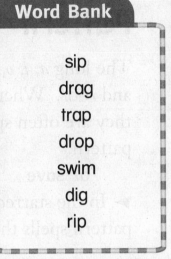

Word Bank

sip

drag

trap

drop

swim

dig

rip

Across

4. My brother and I **pulled**
   the heavy branches.
5. The mountain lion **tore**
   open the tent.
6. The raccoon **drank** water
   from the stream.
7. The boys are **moving** in
   the cold, clear water.

Down

1. My foot was **caught**
   between two rocks!
2. Can you hear the water
   falling?
3. The bear is **searching**
   under the log for grubs.

Name _____

The Vowel-Consonant-*e* Pattern

The long *a, i, o,* and *u* sounds are shown as /ā/, /ī/, /ō/, and /o͞o/. When you hear these sounds, remember that they are often spelled with the vowel-consonant-*e* pattern.

/ā/ s**ave**   /ī/ l**ife**   /ō/ sm**oke**   /o͞o/ h**uge**

► In the starred words *come* and *love*, the *o*-consonant-*e* pattern spells the /ŭ/ sound.

Write each Spelling Word under its vowel sound.

/ā/ or /ī/ Sound

_____

_____

_____

_____

_____

/ō/ or /o͞o/ Sound

_____

_____

_____

_____

No long vowel Sound

_____

_____

Spelling Words

1. smoke
2. huge
3. save
4. life
5. wide
6. come*
7. mine
8. grade
9. smile
10. note
11. cube
12. love*

Name _____

Spelling Spree

Book Titles Write the Spelling Word that best completes each book title. Remember to use capital letters.

1. Sing Every _____ by B. A. Soprano

2. I _____ My Cats and Dogs by

   Ima Petowner

3. Dinosaurs Were _____! by Sy N. Tific

4. Live Your _____ to the Fullest by

   Hy Lee Adventurous

5. _____ to My Party by U. R. Invited

Puzzle Play Write a Spelling Word for each clue. Then write the circled letters in order to spell something you might see over a waterfall.

6. a year of school __ Ⓞ __ __ __

7. to keep for a while __ Ⓞ __ __

8. a happy expression __ __ Ⓞ __ __

9. belongs to me __ __ Ⓞ __

10. one shape for ice __ __ __ Ⓞ

11. fire can cause it __ __ Ⓞ __ __

12. opposite of narrow Ⓞ __ __ __

__ __ __ __ __ __ __

Name _____

Proofreading and Writing

Proofreading Circle the five misspelled Spelling Words in the following notice. Then write each word correctly.

1. smoke
2. huge
3. save
4. life
5. wide
6. come*
7. mine
8. grade
9. smile
10. note
11. cube
12. love*

Attention All Visitors

Our wilderness areas are home to many kinds of animal and plant lif. They provide nesting areas for huje numbers of birds. People com from cities and towns all over the world to camp and hike in the wilderness. Show your respect and luv for the natural world. The children of the future must have the chance to enjoy these wid open spaces too.

1. _____   4. _____

2. _____   5. _____

3. _____

Write a Journal Entry Think about a special time you had outdoors. Where were you? Was it a field trip? A family outing? Or maybe a block party?

On a separate sheet of paper, describe where you were and what was special about the experience. Use Spelling Words from the list.

Name _____

Entry Words

Read the following letter. Then decide whether each under-lined word would be an entry word in a dictionary or part of an entry. Write the word in the correct column below.

Dear Malcolm,

Our <u>camping</u> trip was great! We <u>backpacked</u> across a creek and set up our tents near the water. Then we had a <u>cookout</u> and watched the stars. We heard <u>growling</u> outside our tent, and I was scared. The next morning, we found tracks outside our tent. Dad said it was a <u>mountain lion!</u> The best part of the trip was when we <u>climbed</u> to the top of a huge waterfall. My <u>brother</u> and I were really proud, especially when Mom and Dad made it to the top! You'll have to see the great <u>souvenir</u> I brought back with me the next time you visit.

Your friend,

Rick

Entry Word	**Part of an Entry**
_____	_____
_____	_____
_____	_____
_____	_____

Name _____

Connecting Subjects and Predicates

Read the sentence parts. Write S next to each subject. Write P next to each predicate. Then put the parts together to write six sentences. Write your sentences on the lines below.

a distant owl ___	block our path ___
the pounding water ___	crashes against the rocky
carries her own backpack ___	canyon ___
my father ___	puts on his hiking boots ___
the squirrels and	a few giant boulders ___
chipmunks ___	my sister ___
hoots to the moon ___	collect food on the ground ___

1. _____

2. _____

3. _____

4. _____

5. _____

6. _____

Name _____

Combining Subjects and Predicates

Combine each pair of sentences. Then write the new sentence on the line.

1. The sun shines. The sun heats the air.

   _____

2. My brother sees some animals. I see some animals.

   _____

3. The foxes run away. The deer run away.

   _____

4. We follow the trail. We find a cave.

   _____

5. The cave is dark. The cave is large.

   _____

6. We find our flashlight. We turn it on.

   _____

7. Bats live in caves. Bears live in caves.

   _____

8. Mother reminds us to be safe. Father reminds us to be safe.

   _____

Name _____

Subjects and Predicates

**Write the complete subject and the complete predicate
of each of the following sentences in the correct column.**

1. We went camping.
2. Our new tent is very light.
3. The sunset was beautiful.
4. A full moon glows.
5. My sister woke up at sunrise.
6. She cooked breakfast over the campfire.
7. Our entire family walked to the canyon.
8. The rocky canyon is full of dangerous places.
9. My father and I spotted the waterfall.
10. The rushing water splashed our faces.

Subjects

_____

_____

_____

_____

_____

_____

_____

Predicates

_____

_____

_____

_____

_____

_____

_____

Name _____

Reasons and Facts

**Use this page to plan your explanation. Then number
your reasons or facts in the order you will use them.**

Topic: _____

_____

_____

Topic Sentence: _____

_____

_____

Reason/Fact: _____	Reason/Fact: _____
_____	_____
_____	_____
Reason/Fact: _____	Reason/Fact: _____
_____	_____
_____	_____

Revising to Organize Facts

Read each paragraph. Improve the sentence order by moving one sentence to another part of the paragraph. Circle the sentence and then draw an arrow to show where it belongs.

Paragraph 1

Dandelions are weeds that have a special way of spreading. When dandelions first bloom, their head looks like one circle-shaped blossom. This bright yellow blossom is actually a bunch of tiny flowers, and each flower produces a seed deep inside. The wind carries the seeds across fields, lawns, and city sidewalks. When the dandelion is done flowering, its hidden seeds (about 200 of them!) push out on threadlike stalks to form a puffy, round seed head, and each seed in this puffball has a fuzzy parachute. Wherever the seeds land, new dandelions grow.

Paragraph 2

Every spring, robins get ready to raise their young. They begin by gathering twigs and dry grass, which they carry high up into a tree. The female does most of the nest building. The male robin helps the female keep the eggs safe from harm. In five or six days, the nest is finished. The female robin lays about four eggs and keeps them warm. At last, after about two weeks, the little ones hatch.

Name _____

Choosing the Best Answer

Use the test-taking strategies and tips you have learned to help you answer these questions. You may go back to *The Waterfall* if you need to. This practice will help you when you take this kind of test.

Read each question. Fill in the circle next to the best answer.

1 Why did the family wade through the cold water?

   ○ They wanted to cool off in the heat of the summer.

   ○ The rocks along the creek were too slippery to climb.

   ○ They were looking for the waterfall.

   ○ There was poison oak along the banks of the creek.

2 What was the first clue the family had that a waterfall was nearby?

   ○ They heard a roaring sound.

   ○ They saw a rainbow in the sky.

   ○ They felt the mist spray on their faces.

   ○ They saw a steep rock slope.

3 Why did Dad say, "End of the road," when the family got to the waterfall?

   ○ The trail they were on ended at the waterfall.

   ○ He thought the waterfall was too dangerous to climb.

   ○ The waterfall was as far as he wanted the family to go.

   ○ Once they got to the waterfall, he was ready to go home.

Theme 1: **Off to Adventure!**   53

Name _____

Choosing the Best Answer

continued

4 What happened that made the older boy feel scared before he fell asleep?

○ He heard something in the brush.

○ He thought about climbing the waterfall.

○ He saw a wild animal near the camp.

○ He thought the family was lost.

5 What made the tracks near the family's camp?

○ a deer

○ a grizzly bear

○ a wolf

○ a mountain lion

6 What did the family decide to do after finding the tracks?

○ go back the way they had come

○ return home

○ climb the waterfall

○ contact the park ranger

Name _____

Spelling Review

Write Spelling Words from the list to answer the questions.

1–17. Which seventeen words have short vowels?

1. _____
2. _____
3. _____
4. _____
5. _____
6. _____
7. _____
8. _____
9. _____
10. _____
11. _____
12. _____
13. _____
14. _____
15. _____
16. _____
17. _____

18–25. Which eight words have the vowel-consonant-*e* pattern?

18. _____
19. _____
20. _____
21. _____
22. _____
23. _____
24. _____
25. _____

Spelling Words

1. drum
2. huge
3. last
4. drop
5. class
6. left
7. wide
8. mix
9. send
10. save
11. smell
12. stick
13. note
14. thick
15. hunt
16. thin
17. grade
18. lot
19. cube
20. pond
21. life
22. sock
23. luck
24. shut
25. smile

Name _____

Spelling Spree

Book Titles Write the Spelling Word that best completes each funny book title. Remember to use capital letters.

1. class
2. mix
3. send
4. smell
5. stick
6. pond
7. sock
8. drum
9. huge
10. grade
11. cube
12. smile

Example: *The Great* _____ *from Planet X*

by I. C. Starrs _Escape_

1. *Put an Ice* _____ *in My Glass and Other Science Experiments* by Sy N. Seen

2. *A* _____ *Is a Frown Upside Down* by Mary Timz

3. *My First Day in* _____ *3: A True Story* by Ima Newcomer

4. *The Mystery in the Third Grade* _____ by Minnie Klooz

5. _____ *Us a Post Card* by U. R. A. Riter

6. *Do I* _____ *Cookies?* by I. M. Hungree

1. _____   4. _____

2. _____   5. _____

3. _____   6. _____

One, Two, Three! Write the Spelling Word that belongs in each group.

7. piano, guitar, _____   10. stir, blend, _____

8. big, large, _____   11. shirt, shoe, _____

9. lake, river, _____   12. twig, branch, _____

Proofreading and Writing

Proofreading **Circle the five misspelled Spelling Words below. Then write each word correctly.**

January 12—Today I went on a treasure hunte. I

spent a lott of time looking for the treasure in a thic

grove of trees and near the pond. I didn't have any

luk. Maybe somebody will drap a clue that I will find!

1. _____   4. _____

2. _____   5. _____

3. _____

A Newspaper Article **Write a Spelling Word that means the same as each underlined word or words.**

Jeremy is a 6. <u>skinny</u> boy in Mr. Boyd's third grade
7. <u>group</u>. All of his 8. <u>years of being</u> Jeremy had heard
about a buried treasure. One day he found a 9. <u>short letter</u> in
his attic. It was all that was 10. <u>still around</u> of his grandfather's
things. He 11. <u>closed</u> the door and read. "Keep your eyes
12. <u>all the way open</u>," it said. "Look under the 13. <u>final</u> tree in
the yard." There Jeremy found a journal that he will 14. <u>keep</u>.

6. _____   9. _____   12. _____

7. _____   10. _____   13. _____

8. _____   11. _____   14. _____

Write a Letter **On a separate sheet of paper, write to a friend about a buried treasure you hope to find. Use the Spelling Review Words.**

> ## Spelling Words
>
> 1. lot
> 2. left
> 3. thick
> 4. life
> 5. thin
> 6. last
> 7. luck
> 8. note
> 9. class
> 10. hunt
> 11. drop
> 12. wide
> 13. save
> 14. shut

Name _____

Celebrating Traditions

Describe a tradition that you celebrate. When do you celebrate it? Who shares the celebration with you? What is your favorite part of this tradition?

_____

_____

_____

_____

_____

_____

_____

List any traditions you would like to learn about.

_____

_____

_____

_____

Name _____

Celebrating Traditions

Fill in the chart as you read the stories.

The Keeping Quilt

What tradition is celebrated in this selection?

Why is this tradition important to those who celebrate it?

Anthony Reynoso: Born to Rope

What tradition is celebrated in this selection?

Why is this tradition important to those who celebrate it?

The Talking Cloth

What tradition is celebrated in this selection?

Why is this tradition important to those who celebrate it?

Dancing Rainbows

What tradition is celebrated in this selection?

Why is this tradition important to those who celebrate it?

Name _____

Quilt Crossword

Write the word that matches each clue in the puzzle. Use the vocabulary words for help.

border
gathering
needles
scraps
sewn
threaded

Across

4. edge

6. tools for sewing

Down

1. coming together

2. leftover pieces

3. passed through the eye of a needle

5. put together with a needle and thread

Name _____

Author's Family Chart

Anna's Mother
(author's great-great-grandmother)

1. Table cloth for Sabboth meals.

Anna
(author's great-grandmother)
1. wedding huppa
2. A baby blanket for Car

Carle
(author's grandmother)

1. wedding huppa
2. blanket for Mary Ellen
3. blanket for Old Anna legs.
4. tablecloth for Anna's birthday

Mary Ellen
(author's mother)

1. for special celebrations
2. A blanket for Patrica
3. A cape or tent for Patricias games.
4. for telling the story of the quilt

Patricia Polacco
(author)

1. for special celebrations
2. Superhero cape
3. blanket for Mother who is sick.
4. story of quitt

Why is the quilt important to the author?

It has been used in her family for years to tell about their traditions and celebrations.

Name _____

Piece It Together

Finish each statement with details from *The Keeping Quilt*.

1. Anna's mother decides to make the quilt because

   It will help them remember home,

   (Russia).

2. When Carle grows up, Great-Gramma Anna passes
   the quilt on to her. She

   uses it as a wedding huppa. Then she passes

   it on to Mary Ellen.

3. Over the years, people in the family use the quilt as

   a huppa, a pretendcape, a blanket, a table

   cloth.

4. Mary Ellen tells her daughter (the author) whose

   Whose clothes used to make the

   quilt.

5. Mary Ellen also is lucky enough to tell the story of the quilt to

   her grandchildren and great-grand

   child.

Name _____

An Author's View

Read the story. Then finish the chart on the next page.

Foxtails

When I first saw Grandma Sorensen in her doorway, she seemed ten feet tall and skinny! She frowned as she squinted into the sun and watched our car. Would I like her?

In the living room, Grandma Sorensen gave each of us a big hug. Then she and Mom began talking. Soon they were laughing about things Mom did as a girl. Once she fell out of their apple tree and broke her arm. Then Grandma told how she too had fallen out of an apple tree and broken her arm. That was when she was a girl in Denmark. I said, "I'm never going to climb apple trees!" Grandma laughed.

Later, after Mom had left for a meeting, Grandma suggested that we make my mother a treat, the one she loved best at my age. In the kitchen, Grandma let me mix flour, sugar, eggs, butter, and vanilla together to make a stiff dough. Then she showed me how to pinch off a small piece of dough, roll it, and twist it into a "foxtail." She didn't mind that I made the tails a bit crooked.

As we worked, Grandma asked me about school and what I wanted to be when I grew up. From her questions I could tell she was really interested in what I said. What a good listener! By the time Mom returned, the foxtails were ready to eat, and Grandma and I were best friends.

Name _____

An Author's View continued

Use story details to finish this chart. Tell how the author feels about her grandmother.

Scene	Details About Grandma	Author's Feelings About Grandma
The Doorway	1. Frowned and squinted for car 2. looked ten feet tall.	Looked scary and thought she was evil.
The Living Room	1. Mom and grand ma talke 2. Told stories	Bored. Beggining to like Grand- ma.
The Kitchen	1. Decided to make a treat for Mom 2. Made foxtails.	She devoloped a friendship with Grandma.

If you met Grandma Sorensen, do you think you would like her? Why or why not? Use complete sentences.

At first, I'd be a little scared. But then I'll get used to her.

Name _____

Compound Mix-up

**Write a compound word to match each picture clue.
Each word is made up of two words from the Word Bank.**

Word Bank

dog	bug	pot	lady	flower	flag
fly	dragon	tooth	rain	fish	bow
house	brush	pole	moon	star	light

_____ _____ _____

_____ _____ _____

_____ _____ _____

**Combine two words from the Word Bank to make a new
compound word.**

_____

Name _____

More Long Vowel Spellings

To spell a word with the /ā/ sound, remember that /ā/ can be spelled *ai* or *ay*. To spell a word with the /ē/ sound, remember that /ē/ can be spelled *ea* or *ee*.

| /ā/ | ai, ay | p**ai**nt, cl**ay** |
| /ē/ | ea, ee | l**ea**ve, f**ee**l |

▶ In the starred words *neighbor*, *eight*, and *weigh*, the /ā/ sound is spelled *eigh*.

Write each Spelling Word under its vowel sound.

/ā/ Sound

/ē/ Sound

Spelling Words

1. paint
2. clay
3. feel
4. leave
5. neighbor*
6. eight*
7. seem
8. speak
9. paid
10. lay
11. need
12. weigh*

Theme 2: **Celebrating Traditions**   67

Name _____

Spelling Spree

**Fill in the Blank Write the Spelling Word that best
completes each sentence.**

1. I whisper when I need to _____ softly.

2. My _____ lives across the street.

3. I stand on the scale when I want to _____ myself.

4. My brother formed a bowl out of _____.

5. I set up my easel when I want to _____.

6. One more than seven is _____.

7. I don't want to stay, so I will _____.

1. paint
2. clay
3. feel
4. leave
5. neighbor*
6. eight*
7. seem
8. speak
9. paid
10. lay
11. need
12. weigh*

1. _____   5. _____

2. _____   6. _____

3. _____   7. _____

4. _____

**Letter Swap Write a Spelling Word by
changing the first letter of each word.**

8. peel   _____

9. maid   _____

10. seed   _____

11. say   _____

12. teem   _____

Name _____

Proofreading and Writing

Proofreading Circle the five misspelled Spelling Words in this invitation. Then write each word correctly.

Dear New Neighbor,

　　Please join me and some of the other tenants in the building for a quilting party. I have enough needles and thread for ~~eaght~~ helpers. You don't ~~ned~~ to be a sewing expert. The work will ~~seam~~ easy, and we will all get to know one another. Later we will have tea and cake. The party will be in my apartment next Monday evening. If you are interested, ~~spek~~ to me soon. If you prefer, you can ~~leve~~ a note in my mailbox instead.

　　　　　　　Sincerely,
　　　　　　　Natasha Pushkin

1. paint
2. clay
3. feel
4. leave
5. neighbor*
6. eight*
7. seem
8. speak
9. paid
10. lay
11. need
12. weigh*

1. _eight_
2. _need_
3. _seem_
4. _speak_
5. _leave_

Write a Description If you were going to design a quilt like the one in the story, what would it look like?

On a separate sheet of paper, write about a quilt you would design. Tell what material you would use and why. Use Spelling Words from the list.

Name _____

Word Family Reunion

Select the words that belong to the word family for "back."
Then arrange the words on the chart and define each one.
Check your work in a dictionary.

The Back Family

Word Bank

| backward | bacteria | backyard | bachelor | backboard |
| backbone | backfire | background | backpack | backup |

Word	Meaning
1. _____	_____
2. _____	_____
3. _____	_____
4. _____	_____
5. _____	_____
6. _____	_____
7. _____	_____
8. _____	_____

Name _____

In Search of Common Nouns

Circle the common noun or nouns in each group of words.

1. big   room

2. quilt   sewed   needle

3. house   talk   enjoy   people

4. blanket   warm   sister   friend

5. happy   silly   story   angry

6. curious   city   cheerful   sad

Write the circled nouns in the correct square below.

Persons

_____

_____

Places

_____

_____

Things

_____

_____

_____

Name _____

Common Nouns in Signs

Find the common nouns in the report. Write each common noun in the correct exhibit room below.

A Visit to the Museum

My friends and I visited a museum. There we saw a collection of wonderful old quilts. Some of them were made by pioneers. Many of the blankets showed children, flowers, and trees. One showed all fifty states.

Exhibit Room 1: People

_____

_____

_____

Exhibit Room 2: Places

_____

_____

Exhibit Room 3: Things

_____

_____

_____

_____

_____

Name _____

Commas in a Series

Proofread each sentence. Add commas to separate each series of three or more words. Remove all unnecessary commas.

1. Our attic is filled with boxes bags and books.

   _____

2. I found my great-grandfather's hat gloves and cane.

   _____

3. The cane was carved with tigers lions and elephants.

   _____

4. I also found old journals photographs and drawings.

   _____

5. One photograph shows my aunt uncle and cousin.

   _____

6. My great-grandmother lived on a farm with chickens cows horses and pigs.

   _____

   _____

7. In her diary, she described her, friends relatives and visitors.

   _____

8. Her hopes wishes and dreams, bring every page to life.

   _____

Name _____

Compare-Contrast Paragraphs

Use the chart on this page to help you plan paragraphs that compare and contrast. Write what the paragraphs will be about. Write two or three interesting details that show how the people, places, and things are alike. Then write how they are different. Use the details you record in your writing.

What I Will Compare and Contrast

_____

_____

How They Are Alike

1. _____

2. _____

   _____

3. _____

   _____

How They Are Different

1. _____

   _____

2. _____

   _____

3. _____

   _____

Name _____

Sentence Combining

► Combining short, choppy sentences into compound sentences can make your writing sound smooth and interesting.

► Use a comma and the word *and* to create a compound sentence that makes a comparison.

Example: The gifts were part of the women's bouquets, **and** each gift was a symbol of something important for a good life.

► Use a comma and the word *but* to create a compound sentence that makes a contrast.

Example: At the first weddings, the women wore wedding dresses, **but** later some women wore suits.

Write a compound sentence. Combine the sentences with a comma and the joining word in parentheses ( ).

1. The women loved the keeping quilt. They used it to keep their family's traditions alive. (and)

   The women loved the quilt, and kept the traditions alive, he

2. The women's weddings were alike in some ways. They were also different. (but)

   The women's weddings were alike in some way, but different.

3. The quilt was used as a cape. It was used as a huppa too. (and)

   The quilt was used as a cape, and it was used as a huppa too.

Name _____

Revising Your Instructions

Reread your instructions. What do you need to make them better? Use this page to help you decide. Put a checkmark in the box for each sentence that describes your instructions.

Rings the Bell!

☐ The goal of my instructions is clearly stated.

☐ The steps are clear and in the right sequence.

☐ The information that I presented is complete. I included all the necessary details.

☐ I used exact words to make my directions as precise as possible.

Getting Stronger

☐ I could make the goal of the instructions clearer.

☐ My steps aren't always clear. The sequence may need work.

☐ I need to add some important information.

☐ I could add exact words to improve my instructions.

Try Harder

☐ The goal of my instructions is not stated.

☐ The steps aren't clear, and they are out of order.

☐ I left out some very important information.

☐ I need to use more exact words.

Using Exact Nouns

Circle the letter of the noun that best replaces each underlined word or phrase.

1. Do you want to be a movie <u>person who acts</u>?

   a. lawyer   b. watcher   c. star   d. Venus

2. First, you need to have a good head of <u>fuzzy stuff</u>.

   a. hair   b. ears   c. smile   d. connections

3. Then, you need some cool clothes and a pair of dark <u>eye things</u>.

   a. pupils   b. carrots   c. cups   d. sunglasses

4. Next, you need a big, fancy house with a <u>big thing of water</u>.

   a. garage   b. door   c. pool   d. yard

5. You'll need to eat at all the best <u>eating places</u>.

   a. restaurants   b. stations   c. rinks   d. garages

6. Of course, you need to have an agent and a <u>person who represents you legally</u>.

   a. judge   b. sheriff   c. lawyer   d. partner

7. Do you need any actual acting <u>stuff</u>?

   a. manners   b. talent   c. rules   d. clothes

8. "It helps, but it's not a must," say all the top Hollywood movie <u>leaders</u>.

   a. sleepers   b. sellers   c. drivers   d. directors

Name _____

Spelling Words

Look for spelling patterns you have learned to help you remember the Spelling Words on this page. Think about the parts that you find hard to spell.

Write the missing letters and apostrophe in the Spelling Words below.

1. n ____ ____

2. o ____ ____

3. f ____ r

4. ____ ____ most

5. ____ ____ so

6. can ____ ____

7. ca ____ ____ ot

8. ab ____ ____ t

9. ____ ____ ways

10. ____ ____ day

11. unt ____ ____

12. ag ____ ____ n

Spelling Words

1. now
2. off
3. for
4. almost
5. also
6. can't
7. cannot
8. about
9. always
10. today
11. until
12. again

Study List **On another sheet of paper, write each Spelling Word. Check the list to be sure you spell each word correctly.**

78   Theme 2: **Celebrating Traditions**

Name _____

Spelling Spree

Word Switch **For each sentence, write a Spelling Word to take the place of the underlined word or words.**

1. Let's go ride the roller coaster <u>another time</u>!
2. I'm in a real hurry, so I can't talk <u>at this time</u>.
3. Sofia <u>every time</u> has a box of raisins in her lunch.
4. My mom said that you can come to the beach too, <u>if you want</u>.
5. It's been <u>not quite</u> three years since we had a snowstorm.
6. They said on the radio that the <u>current day</u> is the first day of fall.

1. _____ 4. _____

2. _____ 5. _____

3. _____ 6. _____

Spelling Words

1. now
2. off
3. for
4. almost
5. also
6. can't
7. cannot
8. about
9. always
10. today
11. until
12. again

Letter Math **Add and subtract letters from the words below to make Spelling Words. Write the new words.**

7. foot – ot + r = _____

8. cart – rt + n't = _____

9. able – le + out = _____

10. order – rder + ff = _____

11. canned – ed + ot = _____

12. unit – it + til = _____

Name _____

Proofreading and Writing

Proofreading Find and circle the four misspelled Spelling Words in this poster. Then write each word correctly.

Spelling Words

1. now
2. off
3. for
4. almost
5. also
6. can't
7. cannot
8. about
9. always
10. today
11. until
12. again

> ## Brazilian Festival
>
> On June 15th, the annual Brazilian Festival will take place agin. There will be plenty of traditional music, dancing, and Brazilian food. Our festival is allways a good time. And if you miss this one, you won't get another chance until next year! Tickets are on sale know. Buy yours todday!

1. _____   3. _____

2. _____   4. _____

Write a Poem Think about a tradition that's important to you. It can be one shared by a lot of people, or one that just your family shares. Then write a poem about the tradition. Use Spelling Words from the list.

Name _____

Rodeo Words

**Label each sentence True or False. If the
sentence is false, rewrite it to make it correct.**

1. A rodeo is a sporting event for cowboys.

   True. It is a sporting Event

   _____

2. Ceremonies are a set of acts that honor an event.

   True,

   _____

3. A celebrity is a person who is not very well-known.

   False, They are famous.

   _____

4. An exhibition is a public show or display.

   True,

   _____

5. Experts are people who are beginners at an activity.

   False, Experts are very
   good at things.

6. Performers are people who watch a show.

   False,

   _____

Name _____

Categories Chart

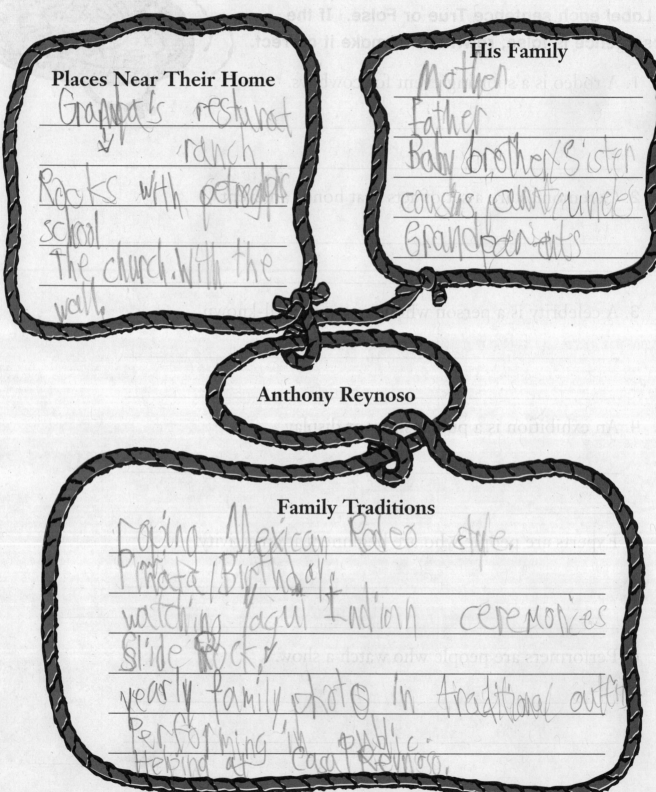

Places Near Their Home

Granpa's resturant ranch
Rocks with petroglphs
school
The church.With the wall.

His Family

Mother
Father
Baby brother/Sister
cousins,aunt,uncles
Grandparents

Anthony Reynoso

Family Traditions

Roping Mexican Rodeo style,
Piñata/Birthday,
watching Yaqui Indian ceremonies
Slide Rock,
yearly family photo in traditional outfit
Performing in public.
Helping at Casa Reynoso.

Name _____

Read All About It!

**Answer the reporter's questions as if you were
Anthony Reynoso. Use complete sentences.**

1. What do you, your father, and your grandfather do on your
grandfather's ranch?

   They help out.

2. Why do you practice roping so much?

   Because it is my tradition I must
   continue.

3. Where do you and your dad often go on Saturdays and
what do you do there?

   Going to Slide Rock.

4. What else do you do in your spare time?

   I practice roping with my father
   in spare time.

5. What special event are you looking forward to? Why?

   The day I become a brother

Name _____

Family Categories

Read the story. Then complete the chart on the next page.

No Time to Spare

It's hard to find a good time to get in touch with my Aunt Mickey Sobol. It's even harder to reach my cousins Karen and Ike. That's because they're always busy.

Their day starts at sunup when Karen and Ike head for the barn to feed their sheep. Meanwhile, Aunt Mickey does chores and fixes the lunches. After breakfast, my cousins take the bus to school, and Aunt Mickey leaves for work.

Each day, Aunt Mickey walks a mile to the little store she runs by the lake. People from nearby vacation homes often stop there, so she's always busy.

After school, Karen and Ike head for the animal shelter down the road. Both of them want to be animal doctors, so they like to help with the animals.

After dinner and homework, the family relaxes. Ike usually reads, and Karen talks to a friend on the computer. Aunt Mickey enjoys weaving colorful blankets made of wool from their sheep.

Name _____

Family Categories

Write story details to complete this chart.

Family Members

Aunt Mikey
Karen
Ike

Places Near Their Home
their barn

little store
vacation homes
animal shelter

The Sobol Family.

Activities
going to school

feeding sheep
shop at store
making blankets
help animals
do homework

Name _____

Perfect Plurals

► Add -*s* to form the plural of most nouns.

hat / hat**s**

► Add -*es* to form the plural of nouns that end in *ch*.

lunch / lunch**es**

► When a noun ends with a consonant and *y*,

change the *y* to *i* and add -*es*.

penn*y* / penn**ies**

**Write the plural of the word that matches each clue
in the puzzle. Use the Word Bank for help.**

Across

2. parts of a tree
5. small horses
7. strong, thick cords
8. lunch items
9. very large sea animals

Down

1. covers for the head
2. small blue fruits
3. activities done for fun
4. groups of parents and their
   children
6. large farms where cattle are
   raised

Name _____

The Long *o* Sound

To spell a word with the /ō/ sound, remember that this sound can be spelled *oa*, *ow*, or *o*.

/ō/   oa, ow, o   c**oa**ch, bl**ow**, h**o**ld

► In the starred words *sew* and *though*, the /ō/ sound is spelled *ew* and *ough*.

Write each Spelling Word under its spelling of the /ō/ sound.

1. coach
2. blow
3. float
4. hold
5. sew*
6. though*
7. sold
8. soap
9. row
10. own
11. both
12. most

oa Spelling

_____

_____

_____

o Spelling

_____

_____

_____

ow Spelling

_____

_____

Another Spelling

_____

_____

Name _____

Spelling Spree

Word Maze Begin at the arrow and follow the
Word Maze to find seven Spelling Words. Write
the words in order.

1. coach
2. blow
3. float
4. hold
5. sew*
6. though*
7. sold
8. soap
9. row
10. own
11. both
12. most

1. _____   5. _____

2. _____   6. _____

3. _____   7. _____

4. _____

Classifying Write the Spelling Word that
belongs in each group of words.

8. have, possess, _____

9. mend, stitch, _____

10. teacher, trainer, _____

11. toothpaste, shampoo, _____

12. lots, many, _____

Name _____

Proofreading and Writing

Proofreading Circle the five misspelled Spelling
Words in this poster. Then write each word correctly.

May 19, Sedona Fairgrounds
Roping Exhibition!

See bothe Reynoso roping champions!

Be ready to holed on to your hats! Thrill to the

tricks of Arizona's moast talented father and son

rope spinners. You won't believe your oun eyes!

Tickets will be soled at the gate.

1. coach
2. blow
3. float
4. hold
5. sew*
6. though*
7. sold
8. soap
9. row
10. own
11. both
12. most

1. _____   4. _____

2. _____   5. _____

3. _____

Write a Story About Yourself Have you ever worked hard to
learn something? Maybe it was learning to swim, ride a bike,
or even tie your shoes.
**On a separate sheet of paper, write about a time when you
worked very hard to learn something. Tell what the experience
was like. Use Spelling Words from the list.**

Word Sort

Parts of a Dictionary Read each word. Then alphabetize
the words and place each word with the correct guide words.

snore	lentil	outing
outfit	outgoing	lent
lesson	snowdrift	outlet
snow	leopard	snout

lengthy/let

_____

_____

_____

snip/snowdrop

_____

_____

_____

outfielder/outnumber

_____

_____

_____

Name _____

Capital Letters

Capitalize each proper noun on the list below.

1. anthony reynoso _____

2. mexico _____

3. tuesday _____

4. fifth avenue _____

5. martha cooper _____

6. fourth of july _____

7. united states of america _____

8. *the keeping quilt* _____

9. mary ellen suarez _____

10. sedona, arizona _____

Write the proper noun or nouns in each sentence.

11. After school, Dad shows me a new rope trick. _____

12. On Saturday, we go to the Sedona Rodeo. _____

13. I read the new book by Ginger Gordon. _____

14. Her first book was *My Two Worlds*. _____

15. She is a teacher in New York City. _____

Name _____

Charting Capital Letters

This chart shows common and proper nouns. Add one more proper noun for each common noun in the chart.

	Common Noun	Proper Noun
people	author	Ginger Gordon _____
	boy	Anthony Reynoso _____
	relative	Dad _____
places	country	Mexico _____
	state	Arizona _____
	city	Guadalupe _____
	street	Elm Street _____
	school	Booker T. Washington Elementary School
things	river	Rio Grande _____
	month	September _____
	day	Wednesday _____
	language	Spanish _____

Proper Nouns

Remember that titles and their abbreviations, when used with a person's name, begin with a capital letter. Use a capital letter for a person's initials. End abbreviated titles with a period.

Proofread the letter below. Find the proper nouns and titles that need capital letters. Look for abbreviations that need periods. Use the proofreading marks to show the correction.

Proofreading Marks	
Make a small letter:	Çity
Make a capital letter:	boston
Add a period:	Mr⨀

Mr. Jason Brown
326 cypress Lane
sedona, AZ 86336

Dear Jason,

    Hello from new mexico! I came here with my friend, mrs williams.

We saw some amazing rope tricks at the rodeo. The

winner of the contest was sheriff paul ortega.

    After the rodeo, we saw some real animals at the santa fe National

Forest. Our tour guide was dr angela t. carson.

    I can't wait to get home and show our pictures to all of you

in mrs walter's class.

                    Bye for now,
                    Martin

Name _____

A Description

Use this page to help you plan your response to the following prompt.

Anthony Reynoso: Born to Rope tells the life story of a young rodeo star. What kind of person is Anthony? Write a description of Anthony Reynoso. Include details about what he looks like, what he does, and what he says.

What He Looks Like	What He Does	What He Says

Name _____

Correcting Run-On Sentences

► Two or more sentences that run together
  make a **run-on sentence**.

► Correct run-on sentences by making separate sentences.
  Add sentence end marks and capital letters where they are needed.

Run-On Sentence:

My friend Patricia loves to dance, she studies ballet every Saturday.

Corrected Sentences:

My friend Patricia loves to dance. **S**he studies ballet every Saturday.

If the sentence is correct, write *Correct*. **If it is a run-on sentence,
write it as two sentences.**

1. My favorite singer is Gloria Estefan, she sings great songs.

   _____

   _____

2. My father runs a restaurant in town, he's the best cook in the world.

   _____

   _____

3. My mother is a math teacher at Yorkstone High School.

   _____

   _____

4. My sister Tasha loves gymnastics, she does the best cartwheels.

   _____

   _____

Name _____

Word Search

Write the letter of the correct definition next to each word. Then find the words in the puzzle and circle them.

1. wealth _____

2. royalty _____

3. collection _____

4. embroidered _____

5. symbols _____

6. flourish _____

a. decorated by sewing

b. kings and queens

c. lots of money or belongings

d. drawings that stand for something

e. a group of items with something in common

f. a showy waving motion

E	M	B	R	O	I	D	E	R	E	D	D	D
K	J	J	M	F	C	O	Q	W	H	R	G	N
O	L	U	J	Y	R	R	O	Y	A	L	T	Y
R	O	Q	I	P	C	C	O	S	H	T	C	A
X	S	L	D	E	E	O	W	V	E	O	J	N
F	P	X	C	C	O	L	L	E	C	T	O	R
H	L	J	J	M	F	L	O	U	R	I	S	H
L	V	I	M	G	C	E	U	U	N	N	J	B
N	E	F	W	I	M	C	P	W	W	D	J	S
S	S	W	E	A	L	T	H	L	P	Z	K	J
S	E	C	J	W	S	I	J	E	L	M	E	L
W	Y	S	Y	M	B	O	L	S	U	R	Q	W
N	T	R	J	B	V	N	D	Y	Y	S	X	O

Name _____

Cluster Maps

Aunt
Phoebe

adinkra
cloth

Name _____

What the Cloth Says

Complete these sentences about *The Talking Cloth*.

Aunt Phoebe tells Amber about many things. Today they

talk about _____. At one

time, only _____ wore it.

Amber learns that the cloth talks because the colors and

symbols _____. If the cloth is

white, that means _____. If it is blue,

that means _____. The symbols on it

stand for ideas like _____ and

_____.

Aunt Phoebe wraps the cloth around Amber. Now she

feels as if she's an _____ with

_____ gathered

around her.

Name _____

Details for Playing

Read the story. Then complete the chart on the next page.

Not for Sale

As Zack walked along, he passed stores with window displays that didn't interest him. Then he came to a store window full of old, worn things. A strange object caught his eye. The wood was dark and shiny smooth. It was long, about as long as Zack's arm, and had six little bowls along each of its sides. At each end was a larger bowl, which made fourteen little bowls in all.

Curious, Zack went inside for a better look. Noting Zack's interest, the shopkeeper explained that the wooden object was a game board carved by an Ashanti artist in Ghana, Africa. The shopkeeper pulled up two chairs and told Zack to sit down. Then he scooped out some brown seeds from one of the bowls and showed Zack how to play *wari*, an Ashanti board game.

At least once a week Zack stopped by the shop to play *wari* with Mr. Oban, the shopkeeper. Both he and Mr. Oban enjoyed playing. And when they finished, Mr. Oban always put the game board away in the back room. It was no longer for sale.

Name _____

Details for Playing

continued

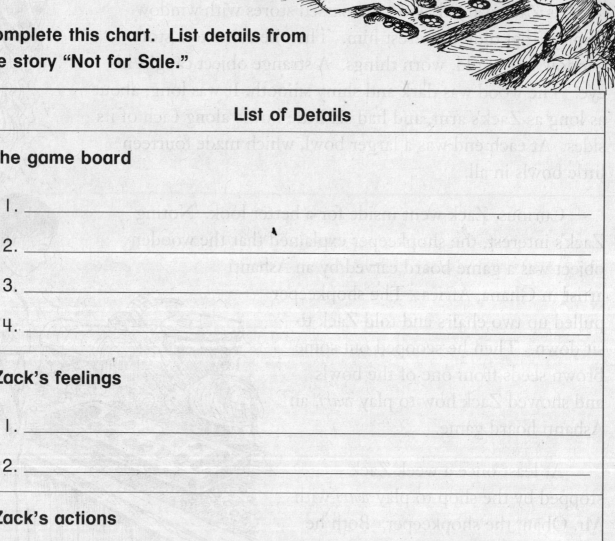

Complete this chart. List details from
the story "Not for Sale."

List of Details
the game board
1. _____
2. _____
3. _____
4. _____
Zack's feelings
1. _____
2. _____
Zack's actions
1. _____
2. _____
3. _____
4. _____

Name _____

Shorten It!

A **contraction** is the short way of saying or writing two words.
The apostrophe (') takes the place of one or more letters.
Fill in the spaces below to show how contractions are formed.

1. he   +   is   =   _____

2. she   +   will   =   _____

3. was   +   not   =   _____

4. they   +   are   =   _____

5. I   +   will   =   _____

6. _____ + _____ = it's

7. _____ + _____ = you're

8. _____ + _____ = hasn't

9. _____ + _____ = isn't

10. _____ + _____ = we're

Name _____

Three-Letter Clusters

When two or more consonants with different sounds are written together, they form a **consonant cluster**. When you are spelling a word that has a consonant cluster, say the word aloud and listen for the different consonant sounds. Remember, some words begin with the consonant clusters *spr*, *str*, and *thr*.

spring   **str**ong   **thr**ow

Some other words have unexpected spelling patterns.

► A beginning /n/ sound may be spelled *kn*, as in **kn**ee. (The *k* is silent.)

► A beginning /r/ sound may be spelled *wr*, as in **wr**ap. (The *w* is silent.)

► A final /ch/ sound may be spelled *tch*, as in pa**tch**. (The *t* is silent.)

Write each Spelling Word under its proper category.

Three-Letter Clusters   **Unexpected Consonant Patterns**

_____   _____

_____   _____

_____   _____

_____   _____

Name _____

Spelling Spree

Hink Pinks Write the Spelling Word that fits the clue and rhymes with the given word.

Example: just-born twins   **new** _____ *two*

1. a ball tossed to a baby   **low** _____

2. jam or jelly   **bread** _____

3. cord for a kite on a day in May   _____ **string**

4. you and two friends on a school holiday   _____ **free**

5. a tidy block to live on   **neat** _____

6. plastic covering on a bottle top   **cap** _____

1. _____   4. _____

2. _____   5. _____

3. _____   6. _____

Finding Words Write the Spelling Words in each of these words.

7. patchwork   _____

8. headstrong   _____

9. kneecap   _____

10. wristwatch   _____

11. knowing   _____

12. writer   _____

Theme 2: **Celebrating Traditions**   103

Proofreading and Writing

Proofreading Circle the five misspelled Spelling Words in this character sketch. Then write each word correctly on the lines below.

Amber's aunt has been everywhere. Aunt Phoebe takes a long trip to a faraway place every springe. She has been to Africa thee times. When she visits a foreign country, she wants to nowe what it is like to live there. Every time she walks down a new street, she likes to wache the people carefully. She notices how they dress and listens to how they speak. Later, she always takes the time to rite to Amber about her experiences. I admire Aunt Phoebe because she is always learning something new.

1. spring
2. knee
3. throw
4. patch
5. strong
6. wrap
7. three
8. watch
9. street
10. know
11. spread
12. write

1. _____   4. _____

2. _____   5. _____

3. _____

Write a Thank-You Note Has a relative or friend ever given you a special or unusual gift? What was it that made it special?

On a separate sheet of paper, write a thank-you note for the gift. Make sure to tell the person you are thanking why the gift is special to you. Use Spelling Words from the list.

Name _____

Rhyming Crossword

Complete the crossword puzzle by writing the correct rhyme for each word. Remember that a rhyming word has the same end sound as another word. Choose your answers from the words in the box.

Vocabulary

trip
map
lace
cause
wealth
silk
smiles
sled
smells
might

Across

2. Object used to go across snow.
   Rhymes with *said*.

3. A happy person does this.
   Rhymes with *miles*.

7. A piece of string used to tie a shoe.
   Rhymes with *face*.

8. Riches. Rhymes with *health*.

9. A voyage. Rhymes with *lip*.

10. Drawings of the earth's surface.
    Rhymes with *traps*.

Down

1. What your nose does.
   Rhymes with *tells*.

4. Strength. Rhymes with *right*.

5. A smooth, shiny fabric.
   Rhymes with *milk*.

6. A reason.
   Rhymes with *pause*.

Name _____

Circling Nouns

Circle each singular common noun in the sentences below. Underline each plural common noun.

1. Aunt Phoebe collects many things.

2. The cloth is embroidered in sections.

3. The fabric has no patches.

4. The patterns show many colors and shapes.

5. Phoebe gave her niece two boxes.

6. Inside, she found two colorful dresses.

Write each plural noun in the correct column below.

Add -s to form the plural

_____

_____

_____

_____

Add -es to form the plural

_____

_____

_____

Name _____

Puzzling Plurals

**Complete the puzzle by writing the plural of each noun.
Each noun is used only once. Some letters are filled in
to help you get started.**

Across

princess _____

basket _____

number _____

thing _____

tale _____

Down

symbol _____

box _____

word _____

pattern _____

dress _____

Name _____

Using Exact Nouns

Write a noun that is more exact than each general noun below.

1. animal _____

2. tree _____

3. food _____

4. container _____

5. group _____

Read each sentence below. Then rewrite the sentence on the line, substituting an exact noun for the general noun or word in parentheses.

6. Amber visited her favorite (person).

_____

7. They shared a hot (drink) together.

_____

8. Phoebe showed Amber a (thing).

_____

9. The (thing) was covered with many (shapes).

_____

10. One (shape) looked like a spinning (circle).

_____

Name _____

Planning a Response to Literature

When you write a response to literature, follow these guidelines.

► Read the question carefully.

► Look for key words to help you decide what information the question is asking for.

► Give facts and examples that explain your answer.

Question: Do you think Aunt Phoebe is an interesting person? Explain why or why not.

Main Idea:

Detail:

Detail:

Detail:

Writing Complete Sentences

A complete sentence contains both a naming part
and an action part.

Naming Part   **Action Part**

Aunt Phoebe   bought the adinkra cloth in Africa.

A sentence fragment is an incomplete sentence that has
just one sentence part.

Fragment (naming part only) The Ashanti people.
Fragment (action part only)   Made adinkra cloths.

A complete sentence begins with a capital letter and ends
with the correct end punctuation.

**Read each item. Write *Complete Sentence* if the sentence
has both a naming part and an action part. If the item is a
sentence fragment, make it a complete sentence by adding
words. Write your complete sentence correctly.**

1. Means gold or riches. _____

_____

2. Amber and her father. _____

_____

3. Aunt Phoebe tells stories to Amber. _____

_____

4. Drinks hot mocha. _____

_____

Name _____

What Do You Think?

Answer the questions below. Use your glossary if you need help.

1. Who are some of your ancestors? Where did they live?

   _____

   _____

2. What could someone do to honor his or her

   parents or family members?

   _____

   _____

3. What is something you have learned by imitating another

   person?

   _____

   _____

4. What can you do to show respect for your teacher?

   _____

   _____

5. How should young people act toward their elders?

   _____

   _____

Name _____

Cluster Diagram

Pages 210–211 Main Idea:

Tewas respect earth.

Details:

1. Dances celebrate summer sun.

2. _____

**Pages 212–213
Main Idea:**

_____

_____

Details:

1. _____

_____

2. _____

_____

Topic:
The Tewas and
Their Dances

**Pages 215–216
Main Idea:**

_____

_____

Details:

1. _____

_____

2. _____

_____

Page 214 Main Idea:

_____

Details:

1. _____

2. _____

Name _____

Feast Day Questions

Answer each question about *Dancing Rainbows*.
Use complete sentences.

1. What is Feast Day?

_____

_____

_____

2. Why do Curt, Andy, and the other Tewa people dance on Feast Day?

_____

_____

3. What sounds might you hear on Feast Day in the plaza?

_____

_____

4. When the Tewas dance, what might you see?

_____

_____

_____

5. What did Andy do for his grandson and other young Tewas?

_____

_____

Name _____

Mainly Ideas

Read the article. Then complete the diagram on the next page.

All About Eagles

How many different kinds of eagles do you think live in the world? If you guessed about sixty, you'd be right. Some kinds of eagles are large and some are small. Most are strong for their size. Some are even strong enough to lift food weighing almost as much as they do!

Eagles have been used as symbols of power and freedom. Some people call them the "king of birds" because of their strength and brave, proud looks. In 1782, the United States of America chose the bald eagle as its national bird.

Bald eagles are among the larger eagles. They can weigh anywhere from eight to thirteen pounds. These great birds can have wings that spread as much as seven feet across! Their heads are covered with white feathers, making them look "bald" from a distance.

Name _____

Dancing Rainbows

Comprehension Skill Topic, Main Idea, and Supporting Details

Mainly Ideas continued

Complete the diagram with facts from "All About Eagles."

Topic: _____

Main Idea: _____

Main Idea: _____

Main Idea: _____

Details: _____

Details: _____

Details: _____

Dancing Rainbows

Structural Analysis
Plurals of Words Ending in
ch, sh, x, s

Name _____

More and More Plurals

Add *-es* to form the plural of a singular noun that ends in *ch, sh, x,* or *s.*

branch/branch**es**   dish/dish**es**   mix/mix**es**   bus/bus**es**

When Dora went on vacation to New Mexico, she sent a letter to her best friend. In each blank, write the plural form of the noun in parentheses ( ).

November 4

Dear Sally,

New Mexico is a beautiful place to visit. When I look out my hotel window, I can see (bush) _____, trees, and mountains. There are rocky deserts too.

Yesterday, we visited two horse (ranch) _____. After I rode a gray pony, we ate our (lunch) _____ while sitting on picnic (bench) _____. I was so hungry that I ate two (sandwich) _____ and drank three (glass) _____ of juice! Then we saw (flash) _____ of lightning and heard (crash) _____ of thunder. A storm was coming! Luckily, we got back to our hotel just before the rain started.

When I come home next week, I'm bringing two (box) _____ with me. Do you have any (guess) _____ about what's inside them?

They're presents for you!

Your friend,

Dora

116   Theme 2: **Celebrating Traditions**

Name _____

The Long *i* Sound

When you hear the /ī/ sound, think of the patterns *igh*, *i*, and *ie*.

/ī/ br**igh**t, w**i**ld, d**ie**

Write each Spelling Word under its spelling of the /ī/ sound.

1. wild
2. bright
3. die
4. sight
5. child
6. pie
7. fight
8. lie
9. tight
10. tie
11. might
12. mind

igh Spelling

_____

_____

_____

_____

ie Spelling

_____

_____

i Spelling

_____

_____

Theme 2: **Celebrating Traditions** 117

Name _____

Spelling Spree

Sentence Pairs Write the Spelling Word that best completes each pair of sentences.

Example: A jet does not fly low. It flies <u>high</u>.

1. These shoes are not loose. They are _____.
2. My sister is not a grownup. She is a _____.
3. A tiger is not tame. It is _____.
4. I will not have cake for dessert. I will have _____.
5. Neither team won. The score was a _____.
6. The sunshine is not dim today. It is _____.
7. He did not tell the truth. He told a _____.

1. wild
2. bright
3. die
4. sight
5. child
6. pie
7. fight
8. lie
9. tight
10. tie
11. might
12. mind

1. _____   5. _____

2. _____   6. _____

3. _____   7. _____

4. _____

Missing Letters Each missing letter fits in ABC order between the other two letters. Write the missing letters to spell a Spelling Word.

Example: e _ g h _ j m _ o c _ e *find*

8. c _ e h _ j d _ f   8. _____

9. l _ n h _ j m _ o c _ e   9. _____

10. e _ g h _ j f _ h g _ i s _ u   10. _____

Name _____

Proofreading and Writing

Proofreading Circle the five misspelled Spelling Words in this page from a travel brochure. Then write each word correctly.

 Visit Beautiful New Mexico!

Come to New Mexico and discover a land of amazing beauty! Explore wonderful deserts bathed in brit sunshine. Hike in our mountains and experience adventure in the wilde! Relax your minde and body at one of our many resorts. Enjoy the siet of colorful hot-air balloons in Albuquerque. Spend a week with us, and you just mieght never go home again! That's no lie.

Spelling Words	
1.	wild
2.	bright
3.	die
4.	sight
5.	child
6.	pie
7.	fight
8.	lie
9.	tight
10.	tie
11.	might
12.	mind

1. _____ 3. _____ 5. _____

2. _____ 4. _____

 Write an Explanation The Tewas believe that the eagle is a special animal that carries messages to earth. If you could wear an animal costume, what animal would you choose to be?

On a separate sheet of paper, tell what animal you would choose and explain why you think this animal is special. Use Spelling Words from the list.

Name _____

Definition Derby

Read the dictionary entry for the word *dance*. Then write sample sentences as directed.

dance (dăns) *verb* **1.** To move with rhythmic steps and motions, usually in time to music. **2.** To move lightly and quickly: *The waves danced in the moonlight.*

◇ *noun* **1.** A set of rhyme steps or motions, usually done in time to music. **2.** A gathering at which people dance. **3.** The art of dancing.

dance (dăns) ◇ *verb* **danced, dancing** ◇ *noun*, *plural* **dances**

1. Write a sentence using the most common meaning of *dance*.

_____

2. Write a sentence using noun definition number 3.

_____

3. Write a sentence using noun definition number 1.

_____

4. Write a sentence using verb definition number 2.

_____

5. Write a sentence using the least common meaning of *dance*.

_____

120   Theme 2: **Celebrating Traditions**

Name _____

Beat the Drum for Plurals

Circle all the plural nouns and write each one in the correctly labeled drum.

1. The Tewa children practice dancing.
2. Men and women prepare for a festival.
3. The skies are clear and blue.
4. Families arrive from many different cities.
5. The parties are about to begin.
6. Loaves of bread are stacked on the table.
7. People stomp their feet.
8. Sweet candies are a special treat.

Change *y* to *i* and add *-es*

Special Plural Forms

Name _____

Completing with Plurals

Complete the story by writing the plural form for each noun in parentheses.

1. The _____ are sunny and clear. (sky)

2. All the relatives help bake many _____ of bread for the feast. (loaf)

3. Many _____ have come to the celebration. (family)

4. At last, six _____ begin to dance. (man)

5. Their _____ fly above the ground. (foot)

122 Theme 2: **Celebrating Traditions**

Name _____

Proofreading for Noun Endings

Proofread the paragraphs below. Find plurals of nouns that are spelled incorrectly. Circle each misspelled plural. Then write each correctly spelled noun on the lines below. Use a dictionary for help.

After sunrise, the Tewa mens and womens gather.
Mothers carry their smiling babys. Fatheres walk with
their sons and daughters. People arrive from many citys.
They look forward to the dances and the storys.

Three childs wear buffalo costumies. They are
dancers. Their feet move in beautiful patternes. After the
dance, everyone feasts on loafs of bread and tasty treats.

Regular	Ends in consonant + *y*	Special plurals
_____	_____	_____
_____	_____	_____
_____	_____	_____

Name _____

Summary

Use this page to plan and organize your summary of *Dancing Rainbows*. When you finish, use the outline to write your summary on a separate sheet of paper.

Main Idea:

← | Supporting Detail: |
| --- |

← | Supporting Detail: |
| --- |

Main Idea:

← | Supporting Detail: |
| --- |

← | Supporting Detail: |
| --- |

Main Idea:

← | Supporting Detail: |
| --- |

← | Supporting Detail: |
| --- |

Name _____

Writing for Your Audience

When you write, keep your audience in mind.
► Ask yourself, *Who will read my writing?*
► Use language that fits your readers.

Formal language is used for school assignments.
Formal: The Tewa show their respect for animals with the Buffalo Dance.

Informal language is used for letters and notes between friends.
Informal: The Tewa are crazy about animals. That's why they do the Buffalo Dance.

The following sentences are written in informal language. Read these sentences. Then rewrite each one in more formal language.

1. Informal: The kids love to hang out in the plaza.
   Formal: _____

2. Informal: Curt's mom bakes tons of bread.
   Formal: _____

3. Informal: Curt's ancestors grew lots of stuff.
   Formal: _____

   _____

4. Informal: The feast is really fun for Curt and his family.
   Formal: _____

Name _____

Filling in the Blank

Use the test-taking strategies and tips you have learned to help you complete fill-in-the-blank items about *The Keeping Quilt*. This practice will help you when you take this kind of test.

Read each item. At the bottom of the page, fill in the circle for the answer that best completes the sentence.

1 **By pointing out that Anna was speaking English in only six months while her parents never learned much of it, the author shows that —**

   (A) Anna was smarter than her parents

   (B) it is easier for young people to learn a new language

   (C) it is important for children to go to school

   (D) Anna's parents wanted to move back to Russia

2 **The author probably believes that it is important to remember your homeland, because in the story she has —**

   (F) Anna's parents speak Russian rather than English

   (G) the neighborhood ladies cut out animals and flowers for the quilt

   (H) a detailed description of Anna's home in Russia

   (J) Anna want a quilt to remind the family of Russia

ANSWER ROWS I (A) (B) (C) (D)   2 (F) (G) (H) (J)

Name _____

Filling in the Blank continued

3 The quilt is not always mentioned in the story, but the author lets the reader know how special it is to Anna by having pictures that show —

(A) the quilt at important events in Anna's life

(B) Anna giving it to her husband as a gift

(C) the quilt as the background in every scene

(D) how Anna makes it into something new and different as she gets older

4 The author has Mary Ellen tell her daughter about the pieces of cloth that went into making the quilt to —

(F) encourage Patricia to make her own quilt

(G) describe how the quilt was made

(H) teach Patricia about her family

(J) explain to Patricia how to recycle old clothes

5 The author ends the story by saying "Traci and Steven were now all grownup and getting ready to start their own lives," so the reader knows that —

(A) the family doesn't need the quilt anymore

(B) the quilt will continue to be used

(C) the author plans to write another book about the quilt

(D) the quilt is too old and worn out for Traci and Steven

ANSWER ROWS 3 (A) (B) (C) (D)   5 (A) (B) (C) (D)
4 (F) (G) (H) (J)

Name _____

Spelling Review

Write Spelling Words from the list to answer the questions.

1–9. Which nine words have the long *a* or long *e* sound?

1. _____   6. _____

2. _____   7. _____

3. _____   8. _____

4. _____   9. _____

5. _____

10–16. Which seven words have the long *o* sound?

10. _____   14. _____

11. _____   15. _____

12. _____   16. _____

13. _____

17–22. Which six words have the long *i* sound?

17. _____   20. _____

18. _____   21. _____

19. _____   22. _____

23–25. Which three words end with these letters?

23. _____tch   24. _____ead   25. _____ap

23. _____   25. _____

24. _____

Spelling Words
1. lay
2. feel
3. hold
4. wild
5. might
6. paint
7. seem
8. patch
9. three
10. own
11. speak
12. need
13. lie
14. most
15. spread
16. float
17. row
18. leave
19. both
20. wrap
21. know
22. mind
23. street
24. bright
25. tie

Name _____

Spelling Spree

Rhyme Time Write the Spelling Word that rhymes with
the word in dark print.

Example: A plump kitty is a ____fat____ **cat.**

1. A nice brain is a **kind** _____.

2. An animal life jacket is a **goat** _____.

3. An unreal piece of clothing is a _____ **lie.**

4. Baby triplets are a **wee** _____.

Word Search Underline the eight hidden
Spelling Words. Then write the words.

Example: abeneedlean ____needle____

5. redawildell   9. teriloneedum

6. ymightaledfl   10. grpatchibror

7. enrstreetalp   11. olgeraspread

8. knpaintilke   12. wrilleavekn

5. _____   9. _____

6. _____   10. _____

7. _____   11. _____

8. _____   12. _____

Spelling Words

1. paint
2. leave
3. might
4. need
5. mind
6. tie
7. spread
8. float
9. three
10. wild
11. patch
12. street

Name _____

Proofreading and Writing

Proofreading Circle the six misspelled Spelling Words in this play. Then write each word correctly.

Grandpa: Let's rapp the gifts in brite yellow paper.

Joe: We can laye it on the table for Mom.

Grandpa: Be careful how you hoald it.

Joe: You kno we bouth did a good job!

1. _____   3. _____   5. _____

2. _____   4. _____   6. _____

Complete a Letter Use Spelling Words to complete the following letter.

Thanksgiving makes me 7. _____ very
happy. Our family has its 8. _____ traditions.
My grandfather will 9. _____ his 10. _____
about sharing with others. A feast will 11. _____
on the table, with many plates in a 12. _____.
The 13. _____ simple dishes 14. _____
even tastier then.

Write a Description On a separate sheet of paper, describe a celebration you enjoy. Use the Spelling Words.

Spelling Words

1. lay
2. most
3. wrap
4. lie
5. feel
6. seem
7. hold
8. speak
9. own
10. bright
11. row
12. both
13. know
14. mind

Name _____

It's Tricky!

Compare the three trickster tales.

► Draw a cover cartoon for each tale.
► Write enough about the story to make someone want to read it.

    For example:

    Rabbit races Turtle.

    But in the end, Turtle wins!

    How does slow Turtle beat
       fast Rabbit?

Aunt Fox and the Fried Fish

What happend to all the fish?

Hungry Spider

Will turtle get revenge on spider?

Rabbit Races with Turtle

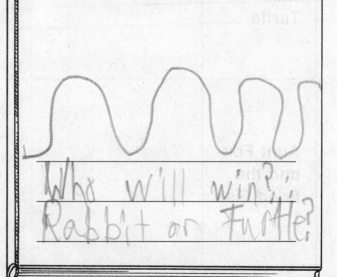

Who will win? Rabbit or Turtle?

Theme 2: **Focus on Trickster Tales**   133

Name _____

What Makes a Trickster Tale?

After reading each selection, complete the chart below to tell why each story is a trickster tale.

	Name the tricksters	Who was tricked?	What was the trick?
Hungry Spider	Spider Turtle	Turtle Spider	Turtle washed his feet and spider ate the food.
Rabbit Races with Turtle	Turtle	Rabbit.	Turtle got his relatives and tricked Rabbit.
Aunt Fox and the Fried Fish	Aunt Fox	Uncle Tiger Uncle Fox	Aunt Fox ate all the fish she scares Uncle Tiger away

Name _____

Incredible Stories

What do you think makes a story incredible? Is it the characters, the setting, or the events? Complete the web with words or phrases that describe an incredible story.

Incredible Stories

Now list some books, movies, or real events that you think are incredible.

_____

_____

_____

_____

Name _____

Incredible Stories

Fill in the chart as you read the stories.

	What incredible thing happens?	How do the characters respond?
Dogzilla		
The Mysterious Giant of Barletta		
Raising Dragons		
The Garden of Abdul Gasazi		

Name _____

Monster Words

Circle the two words that are most alike in meaning.

1. colossal
   small
   big

2. animal
   creature
   tree

3. strong
   brave
   heroic

4. huge
   monstrous
   bad

5. enormous
   terrifying
   scary

6. tremendous
   tiny
   large

7. frightening
   fun
   horrifying

8. little
   tremendous
   colossal

9. terrifying
   horrifying
   monstrous

10. colossal
    heroic
    monstrous

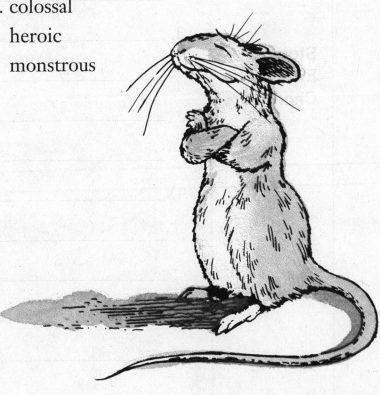

Fantasy and Realism Chart

Story Events and Characters	Fantasy (Make Believe)	Realism (True-to-Life)
	1. A city is built and run _____ _____	1. The wind carries the scent _____ _____
	2. _____ _____ _____	2. _____ _____ _____
	3. _____ _____ _____ _____	3. _____ _____ _____ _____
	4. _____ _____ _____	4. _____ _____ _____
	5. _____ _____ _____	5. _____ _____ _____

Name _____

Fix the Facts

**Read this newspaper story about *Dogzilla*, and draw a line
through the mistakes. Then write what really happened.**

Monster Makes News!

The people in Mousopolis took part in a Cook-Off. It
was winter, and smoke lifted over the city. Soon a strange
sound was heard: "Quack . . . quack." Then Dogzilla
climbed out of a cave!

The troops were sent out. But Dogzilla hid, and the
troops danced home. Dogzilla wandered the city looking
for a place to sleep. The mice called a meeting. The mice decided the only
way to defeat Dogzilla was to think like a donkey. So they munched grass
and waited. It worked! Dogzilla ran out of town. And the problem was solved
forever.

_____

_____

_____

_____

_____

_____

Name _____

A Real Fantasy

Read the story. Find parts that are fantasy and parts that could happen in real life.

A Fish Tale

Way up north, it's cold and dark for much of the year. But that's how polar bears like it, or at least, that's what people think.

"I hate the cold and dark," said Ursa Bear from her seat by the fire. "I want to go where it's warm!"

"That's silly!" snapped her sister. "Now go catch some fish for dinner."

Soon Ursa sat by the ocean's edge, waiting. Her first catch was a mackerel with shiny scales.

"Please don't eat me," begged the fish. "If you let me go, I'll grant you one wish!"

"Can you do that?" asked Ursa. "Then I wish I were somewhere sunny and warm! Here, my friend, I'll let you go."

At once Ursa found herself on a sunny beach next to some surprised people. "This is great!" she cried. "Now where can I find a beach chair?"

The mackerel was even happier. "That's the tenth bear I've wished away today!" he laughed. "Soon my fish friends and I will be all by ourselves."

140   Theme 3: **Incredible Stories**

Name _____

A Real Fantasy continued

Finish the chart. List five fantasy details and five realistic details from the story.

Fantasy Details (make-believe)	Realistic Details (true-to-life)
1. _____ _____	1. _____ _____
2. _____ _____	2. _____ _____
3. _____ _____	3. _____ _____
4. _____ _____	4. _____ _____
5. _____ _____	5. _____ _____

Dogzilla

Structural Analysis Forming
Plurals of Nouns Ending in
f or *fe*

Name _____

Plurals Puzzle

**Write the plural noun that matches each clue in the puzzle.
Use the Word Bank and a dictionary for help.**

Word Bank

thief	cliff	life	safe	wolf
wife	calf	shelf	belief	half

Across
1. Wild animals
2. Young cows
3. Ledges to hold things
5. People who steal
8. Opinions

Down
1. Married women
2. Steep rock walls
4. A cat has nine of these
6. Two equal parts of a whole
7. Containers used for protecting valuable items

Name _____

The Vowel Sounds in *clown* and *lawn*

The /ou/ sound you hear in *clown* can be spelled with the pattern *ow* or *ou*. The /ô/ sound you hear in *lawn* can be spelled with these patterns: *aw*, *o*, or *a* before *l*.

/ou/ cl**ow**n, s**ou**nd

/ô/ l**aw**n, cl**o**th, t**a**lk

► In the starred word *would*, *ou* does not spell the /ou/ sound. Instead, *ou* spells the vowel sound you hear in the word *book*.

Write each Spelling Word under its vowel sound.

/ou/ Sound

_____
_____
_____
_____
_____

/ô/ Sound

_____
_____
_____
_____
_____

Another Vowel Sound

_____

Spelling Spree

Name _____

Hidden Words Write the Spelling Word that is hidden in each group of letters. Do not let the other letters fool you.

Example: e t i t o w n p e   *town*

1. p r e s o f t a c   _____

2. c h a l s o g h e r   _____

3. l a n r c l o t h   _____

4. r e c l o w n e f   _____

Letter Swap Change the underlined letter in each word to make a Spelling Word. Write the Spelling Word.

Example: s<u>h</u>all   *small*

5. court   _____   9. tall   _____

6. dawn   _____   10. world   _____

7. crows   _____   11. low   _____

8. south   _____   12. <u>m</u>ound   _____

Spelling Words

1. clown
2. lawn
3. talk
4. sound
5. cloth
6. would*
7. also
8. mouth
9. crown
10. soft
11. count
12. law

Name _____

Proofreading and Writing

Proofreading Circle the five misspelled Spelling Words. Then write each word correctly.

WARNING TO MICE!

The monster has had puppies! At last cownt, six had been seen. They are now in the city. Do not think of these dogs as sawft and cute. They tore up a laun! They chewed up some kloth! Many mice woud fit in one puppy's mouth. So if you see one, run!

Spelling Words

1. clown
2. lawn
3. talk
4. sound
5. cloth
6. would*
7. also
8. mouth
9. crown
10. soft
11. count
12. law

1. _____   4. _____

2. _____   5. _____

3. _____

Write a Comparison How big is a mouse? How big is a dog? What does a mouse eat? What does a dog eat? How many feet does each animal have? What are their tails like?

On a separate piece of paper, write a comparison of a dog and a mouse. Tell how they are alike and how they are different. Use Spelling Words from the list.

Name _____

Find Meaning Using Context

Choose the correct definition for each of the underlined words in the passage. Write the letter of the definition after the number of the word it matches. Use context clues to help you.

a. ran away, fled

b. frightened, alarmed

c. helpful, constructive

d. enjoyment, pleasure

e. shiver or shake

f. relating to a very early time before events were written down

g. carved, as a design on metal or glass

h. very bad, terrible

i. extremely deep place

j. call forth, gather together

All at once, the volcano began to <u>tremble</u> and rumble. Up
from the <u>depths</u> of the earth came the <u>dreadful</u> Dogzilla! This
monster was millions of years old, from <u>prehistoric</u> times. The
mice didn't think they could teach it to do anything <u>positive</u> for
their town. Using all the courage they could <u>muster</u>, the mice
approached Dogzilla. They hit her with a blast of warm, sudsy
water. The panicking pooch took off at <u>top speed</u>. Delighted,
the Big Cheese watched with <u>relish</u> as Dogzilla <u>hightailed</u> it
out of town. The scary memory of the bubble bath was <u>etched</u>
in Dogzilla's mind forever.

1. _____   4. _____   7. _____

2. _____   5. _____   8. _____

3. _____   6. _____   9. _____   10. _____

Name _____

Writing Possessive Nouns

Rewrite each phrase, using a possessive.

1. the barbecue of the mouse

_____

2. the behavior of the animal

_____

3. the barbecue of the mice

_____

4. the shouts of the mayor

_____

5. the smoke of two volcanoes

_____

6. the shouts of the citizens

_____

7. the tail of the cat

_____

8. the cries of the soldiers

_____

9. the dog belonging to the Smiths

_____

10. the dog belonging to Abigail

_____

Name _____

Finding the Possessive

On the line provided, write the noun in parentheses as a possessive noun to complete each sentence. Then write S if the possessive noun is singular, and P if it is plural.

1. The _____ pictures dazzle the reader. (artist) ____

2. I think that the _____ interest will be high. (readers) ____

3. An _____ imagination is clear on every page. (illustrator) ____

4. The _____ expression looks like a smile. (dog) ____

5. At the end of the story, the _____ faces are adorable. (puppies) ____

6. Most _____ faces aren't that cute! (monsters) ____

7. Every _____ reaction will be a little different. (reader) ____

8. All of the _____ actions were ridiculous. (characters) ____

9. I think that our _____ favorite character is Dogzilla. (class) ____

10. The book was awarded a prize by the _____ committee. (teachers) ____

Name _____

Apostrophes

Rewrite each of the following sentences, adding apostrophes to each incorrectly spelled possessive noun.

1. How would Dav Pilkeys book be different if it were called *Frogzilla*?

   _____

   _____

2. The city would be crushed by Frogzillas huge feet.

   _____

   _____

3. The new heros name might be Dennis the Fly.

   _____

   _____

4. What do you think the flys strategy would be?

   _____

   _____

5. What are the frogs weaknesses?

   _____

   _____

Name _____

Writing a Journal Entry

Think about a memorable experience that happened to you recently. List what happened in order in the chart. Then answer the questions.

Topic of journal entry: _____

```
┌─────────────────────────────────────────────┐
│                                             │
│                                             │
│                                             │
└─────────────────────────────────────────────┘
                      ↓
┌─────────────────────────────────────────────┐
│                                             │
│                                             │
│                                             │
└─────────────────────────────────────────────┘
                      ↓
┌─────────────────────────────────────────────┐
│                                             │
│                                             │
│                                             │
└─────────────────────────────────────────────┘
```

1. What vivid details do you remember about the people, places, things, or events? _____

_____

2. What were your feelings during the experience? _____

_____

Name _____

Journal Entry

Writing without voice sounds boring and doesn't show how you feel about your topic. Your journal entry is about you, and it should sound like you, too! Writing with voice lets you hear the person behind the words.

Weak Voice: We were scared when Dogzilla came out of the volcano.
Strong Voice: Oh, no! It was a giant monster of a dog—Dogzilla!

Weak Voice: I was glad to see Dogzilla leave Mousopolis.
Strong Voice: Thank goodness! Dogzilla was gone!

The sentences below sound flat. Rewrite each sentence to add voice. Use details, words, phrases, and dialogue to make the sentences come alive. (You may write more than one new sentence for each.)

1. Today my mom woke me up early to do my paper route.

   _____

2. My friend and I traded sandwiches at lunch.

   _____

3. I finally finished the book I've been reading.

   _____

Name _____

Revising Your Story

Reread your story. What do you need to make it better? Use this page to help you decide. Put a checkmark in the box for each sentence that describes your personal narrative.

Rings the Bell!

☐ The beginning catches the reader's interest.

☐ My plot is well developed and will hold the reader's attention.

☐ My characters are interesting. I used many details.

☐ I told enough so the reader can picture the setting.

☐ There are almost no mistakes.

Getting Stronger

☐ The beginning could be more interesting.

☐ My plot isn't always clear. Some parts need more explanation.

☐ The ending doesn't really tell how the problem was solved.

☐ I need to add more details.

☐ There are a few mistakes.

Try Harder

☐ The beginning is boring.

☐ The problem is not clear. I did not tell how it was solved.

☐ I need details that tell about my character and the setting.

Name _____

Using Possessive Nouns

A **possessive noun** shows ownership.
► Add *'s* to make a noun possessive.
► Add just an **'** (apostrophe) to make a plural
   noun that ends with *s* a possessive noun.

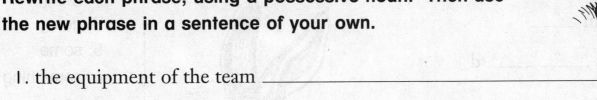

**Rewrite each phrase, using a possessive noun. Then use
the new phrase in a sentence of your own.**

1. the equipment of the team _____

_____

_____

2. the teamwork of the players _____

_____

_____

3. the orders of the coach _____

_____

_____

4. the roar of the audience _____

_____

_____

5. the songs of the cheerleaders _____

_____

_____

Name _____

Spelling Words

Look for spelling patterns you have learned to help you remember the Spelling Words on this page. Think about the parts that you find hard to spell.

Write the missing letters in the Spelling Words below.

1. an _____

2. s _____ _____ d

3. go _____ _____

4. go _____ _____ _____

5. s _____ me

6. som _____ thing

7. y _____ _____

8. y _____ _____ _____

9. fr _____ _____ nd

10. s _____ _____ ool

11. w _____ ere

12. m _____ _____ elf

Study List On another sheet of paper, write each Spelling Word. Check the list to be sure you spell each word correctly.

Name _____

Spelling Spree

The Third Word **Write the Spelling Word that belongs in each group.**

1. I, me, _____

2. plus, also, _____

3. talked, spoke, _____

4. pal, buddy, _____

5. their, our, _____

6. moves, runs, _____

Sentence Fillers **Write the Spelling Word that makes the most sense in each sentence below.**

7. Do you know _____ soccer practice is tomorrow?

8. I have _____ books about bears that I bought last summer.

9. Our _____ usually lets out at 3 o'clock.

10. When is your class _____ to the library?

11. My brother wrote _____ in my notebook, but I can't read it.

12. Have _____ seen my pet snake anywhere?

Spelling Words

1. and
2. said
3. goes
4. going
5. some
6. something
7. you
8. your
9. friend
10. school
11. where
12. myself

Theme 3: **Incredible Stories**   155

Name _____

Proofreading and Writing

Proofreading Circle the four misspelled Spelling Words in the story. Then write each word correctly.

Spelling Words

1. and
2. said
3. goes
4. going
5. some
6. something
7. you
8. your
9. friend
10. school
11. where
12. myself

Yesterday, I was on my way into skool when I heard something rustling in the bushes. I turned around an went over to see what it was. I looked in the spot were I had heard the noise, but there was nothing there. Then, from behind me, a voice sed, "Are you looking for me?" I turned around and found myself face to face with a fox with a sly grin on its face.

1. _____   3. _____

2. _____   4. _____

Incredible Sentences Write four sentences that tell about something incredible. Use a Spelling Word from the list in each one.

Name _____

What Do These Words Mean?

Look up each word in your glossary. Then, in the box above each word, draw a picture that shows the meaning of the word.

giant	pedestal	weakling

statue	square	mysterious

(Hint: Not the shape! Use your glossary for help.)

Name _____

Action Plan

Problem (pages 298–299)	
Action Plan for Solving the Problem (pages 302–308) **Follow these directions:**	
Townspeople	**Mysterious Giant**
1. Find an _____. 2. _____ 3. Don't ask _____ _____ .	1. Take the _____ from Zia Concetta. 2. _____ 3. Travel three miles outside the city and _____. 4. _____ _____ _____ 5. Tell the army that _____ _____ _____ . 6. Return to Barletta.

Name _____

Remember the Details

Think about *The Mysterious Giant of Barletta*. Then complete the sentences.

1. The people of Barletta show their love for the Mysterious Giant by

   _____

   _____

2. The peaceful time for Barletta is over when

   _____

3. Zia Concetta and the Giant figure out a plan to save Barletta. The plan is

   _____

   _____

4. After the soldiers hear what the Giant says, they wonder

   _____

   _____

5. The army captain decides there is only one thing to do, so they

   _____

   _____

Theme 3: **Incredible Stories**   159

Name _____

Directions for Fun

Read the directions. Then answer the questions on the next page.

Fingertip Puppets

Act out your favorite folktale or story using puppets you've made yourself. It's easy and fun to do. All you need are an old rubber glove, scissors, glue, marking pens, and some craft supplies.

First, find an old rubber glove that can be cut apart. Each finger will become a puppet. Draw a line about 2 ½ inches below each fingertip of the glove. Cut along the line and then turn the fingertip inside out.

Next, make the puppet look special. Draw a funny face on your puppet. Then glue on hair made from cotton or yarn. Finally, glue on a hat, shirt, or collar made with pieces of felt. You may also want to add beads, buttons, or trims.

Name _____

Directions for Fun continued

Answer each question about making a fingertip puppet.

1. What supplies will you need?

_____

_____

2. After you find an old rubber glove, what do you do?

_____

_____

3. Why should you draw the line before you cut?

_____

_____

4. After you cut off the fingertip, what should you do next?

_____

_____

5. What should you do before you glue on the hair?

_____

_____

Giant Endings

Fill in each blank using the base word and the ending *-er* or *-est*. The base words are in dark type. To solve the puzzle, write the numbered letter from each answer on the line with the matching number.

1. The statue was the ___ ___ ___ ___ ___ ___ ___ thing
                                               5

   in Barletta. **(tall)**

2. The statue had been in the square ___ ___ ___ ___ ___ ___
                                                                  7

   than anyone could remember. **(long)**

3. To the Giant, late nights were the ___ ___ ___ ___ ___ ___
                                                  1

   time of all. **(nice)**

4. The town was ___ ___ ___ ___ ___ ___ ___ at night
                            3

   than at any other time. **(quiet)**

5. The army was ___ ___ ___ ___ ___ ___ ___ ___ than
                            2   6

   the people of Barletta. **(strong)**

6. The torches were ___ ___ ___ ___ ___ ___ ___ ___
                                       4

   than ever. **(bright)**

The Mysterious Giant has a lot of:

___ ___ ___ ___ ___ ___ ___
1 2 3 4 5 6 7

Name _____

Vowel + /r/ Sounds

**Remember these spelling patterns for the
vowel + /r/ sounds:**

Patterns		Examples
/är/	**ar**	dark
/îr/	**ear**	clear
/ôr/	**or**	north
/ûr/	**er**	her
	ir	girl
	ur	turn
	or	work

**Write each Spelling Word under its vowel + /r/
sounds.**

1. girl
2. clear
3. her
4. turn
5. dark
6. work
7. smart
8. word
9. hurt
10. serve
11. north
12. third

/är/ Sounds

_____

_____

/îr/ Sounds

_____

_____

/ôr/ Sounds

_____

/ûr/ Sounds

_____

_____

_____

_____

_____

Name _____

Spelling Spree

Questions Write a Spelling Word to answer each question.

1. What direction is opposite to south?
2. How do you feel when you solve a hard problem?
3. What might a car do at a street corner?
4. What do you call a sky without clouds?
5. What is it like outside after sunset?
6. What comes between second and fourth?

1. _____   4. _____

2. _____   5. _____

3. _____   6. _____

Missing Letters Each missing letter fits in ABC order between the other letters. Write the missing letters to spell a Spelling Word.

Example: g __ i   n __ p   q __ s   m __ o   *horn*

7. r __ t   d __ f   q __ s   u __ w   d __ f   _____

8. g __ i   d __ f   q __ s   _____

9. v __ x   n __ p   q __ s   j __ l   _____

10. f __ h   h __ j   q __ s   k __ m   _____

11. v __ x   n __ p   q __ s   c __ e   _____

12. g __ i   t __ v   q __ s   s __ u   _____

Name _____

Proofreading and Writing

Proofreading Circle the four misspelled Spelling Words below. Then write each word correctly.

Here is a good way to reach Barletta. Head noarth from Naples. At the edge of town, turn right onto the main highway. This road should be pretty cleer. Take the therd exit after you reach the coast. You should get to Barletta before darck.

Spelling Words

1. girl
2. clear
3. her
4. turn
5. dark
6. work
7. smart
8. word
9. hurt
10. serve
11. north
12. third

_____ _____

_____ _____

Write a Description If you were to make a statue, who would be your subject? Where would it stand so others could see it?

On a separate sheet of paper, write a description of your statue. Tell where it will be placed. Use Spelling Words from the list.

Name _____

Which Meaning Is Correct?

From the definitions below, choose the correct meaning for the underlined word in each sentence. Write the number of the meaning in the blank provided.

---

bargain *noun* **1.** An agreement between two sides; deal: *We made a bargain to split the chores.* **2.** Something offered or bought at a low price: *The book was a bargain at 25 cents.*

hail *verb* **1.** To greet or welcome by calling out: *We hailed our friends as they got off the bus.* **2.** To call or signal to: *I hailed a taxi at the corner* **3.** To congratulate by cheering: *The crowd hailed the hero's return.*

settle *verb* **1.** To arrange or decide upon: *Let's settle the argument today.* **2.** To come to rest: *The leaf settled on the grass.* **3.** To make a home or place to live in: *Pioneers settled on the prairie.*

---

1. Every day, the townspeople <u>hailed</u> the Mysterious Giant as they walked to the market. _____

2. They asked the statue to help them find a good <u>bargain</u> at the market. _____

3. Doves flew to the statue and <u>settled</u> on his head. _____

4. The Mysterious Giant was <u>hailed</u> as a hero. _____

Name _____

Circling Verbs

Circle the verb in each sentence.

1. The giant statue stands in the center of town.

2. People often look at the statue.

3. Everyone loves the statue.

4. Zia Concetta is the oldest person in Barletta.

5. One day, an enemy army approaches the town.

6. Everyone fears the army of powerful soldiers.

7. The soldiers march toward the town.

8. The mysterious statue hops off his pedestal.

9. He asks for three special things.

10. The giant statue cries because of the onion's smell.

Name _____

Finding Verbs

Find the verb in each sentence, and write it on the line at the right.

1. In this story, the giant statue leaps off its pedestal. _____

2. The people believe in the giant. _____

3. Clearly, the giant cares about the town of Barletta. _____

4. Unfortunately, an army attacks the town. _____

5. The people quickly identify the trouble. _____

6. With a little thought, the giant solves the problem. _____

7. He cuts an onion into two pieces. _____

8. The tears run down his face. _____

9. The army fears the giant and his friends. _____

10. At the end of the story, the soldiers leave town. _____

Use this chart to classify the verbs from the sentences above.

Physical Action	Mental Action
_____	_____
_____	_____
_____	_____
_____	_____

Name _____

Using Exact Verbs

Circle the verb in each sentence. Then think of an exact verb to make the sentence more interesting. Rewrite the sentence using your exact verb.

1. An army of powerful soldiers appears.

   _____

2. One night, Zia Concetta goes to the statue.

   _____

3. The giant statue moves off the pedestal.

   _____

4. The statue's clever plan beats the large army.

   _____

5. Today, the statue still is in Barletta, Italy.

   _____

Name _____

Writing a Thank-You Note

Write the gift or kind act you want to thank someone for in the top box. Write details about the gift or kind act in the other boxes.

Who I want to thank: _____

> **Gift or Kind Act:**
>
>
>

> **Detail:**
>
>
>
>

> **Detail:**
>
>
>
>

Name _____

Using Commas for Direct Address

What if in all the excitement at Barletta, no one remembered to thank the vegetable store owner for supplying the very important onion?

Suppose that the thank-you note has now been written, but it needs proofreading. Read the note. Add commas where they belong, before or after the name of the person being addressed.

Dear Sir,

   We the people of Barletta thank you for supplying the onion that made our giant cry! Sir without your onion, our whole plan might have failed miserably. We were ready to run from Barletta, but you Sir stayed bravely in your shop, guarding your vegetables. When your city needed you, you were ready Sir. When we said, "Sir find us an onion," you knew just what to do. Now everyone will always say that it was because of you and your onion that Barletta was saved. Sir you have reason to be proud!

                                        Sincerely,
                                        The Mayor

Name _____

Farm Words

Vocabulary

appetite
chores
harvested
hitched
plow
sown
tended

Write each word next to its definition.

1. gathered or picked _____

2. planted _____

3. hunger _____

4. jobs _____

5. break up and turn over dirt _____

6. took care of _____

7. tied or fastened _____

Write sentences to answer these questions.

8. When you have a big appetite, what do you do?

_____

9. What kinds of fruits or vegetables have you harvested?

_____

10. What are your favorite chores? What chores don't you like to do?

Name _____

Conclusions Chart

Story Details		Story Details		Conclusion
(page 320) Pa raises corn, peas, barley, wheat, and many farm animals.	+	(Page 320) _____ _____ _____ _____	=	Pa _____ _____ _____ _____
(page 323; it's not a rock.) _____ _____	+	(page 325) _____ _____ _____	=	(What's in Miller's Cave) _____ _____
(page 328; Hank's size) _____ _____	+	(Page 328) _____ _____ _____	=	(What Hank looks like) _____ _____
(page 334) _____ _____	+	(page 337) _____ _____	=	(Hank's fate) _____ _____

Name _____

The Dragon's Tale

Tell what happened in *Raising Dragons*.
Complete each sentence to finish the story.

One day a little girl found what looked like a big rock. It was

an egg. She kept wondering _____

_____.

One night she heard _____.

Then the little girl saw _____.

Of course, the girl loved Hank. Each day she fed him and

_____.

Soon he was part of their lives.

Hank helped around the farm. He saved Ma's tomatoes. He

also saved the corn by _____

_____.

Then Hank got too much attention. So the girl took Hank to

_____. She knew

Hank could live there because _____

_____

But Hank surprised the little girl with _____

_____

Name _____

Conclusions from Clues

Read these details about dragons. Then fill in the chart on the next page.

What Dragons Are Really Like

► Dragons have skin much like snakes, lizards, and other reptiles. Since they are cold-blooded, dragons like to live in warm spots.

► Each spring, dragons lay eggs in nests they build. Their nests are made from the same materials that birds use.

► Dragons can fly, but their wings are not at all like birds' wings. They are more like large, leathery bat wings.

► Usually, dragons will not harm people. They only eat frogs, bugs, and fish. Some dragons have been trained to be useful. They pull plows and do other tasks that horses do.

► Dragons do not breathe fire. However, their teeth are larger than a shark's, and they will use them to keep their babies safe.

Name _____

Conclusions from Clues continued

Read each conclusion. Decide if it is correct, and write YES or NO. Write the clues that helped you decide.

Conclusions	Correct Conclusion? (Yes or No)	Story Clues
Dragon skin is scaly.	_____	_____
Dragon nests are made of twigs, sticks, and grasses.	_____	_____
Dragon wings have feathers.	_____	_____
Dragons can be trained to carry riders.	_____	_____
Dragons never bite.	_____	_____

Happy Endings

Choose a word from the box to match each picture clue.
Write the word on the line.

Word Bank

proudly	brightly	leaky	cloudy	beastly
furry	lovely	bumpy	rainy	hairy

1. + y = ___ ___ ___ ___ ___

2. + ly = ___ ___ ___ ___ ___ ___ ___ ___

3. + y = ___ ___ ___ ___ ___ ___

4. + ly = ___ ___ ___ ___ ___ ___ ___

5. + y = ___ ___ ___ ___ ___

6. + ly = ___ ___ ___ ___ ___ ___

Name _____

The /j/, /k/, and /kw/ Sounds

► The /j/ sound can be spelled with the consonant *j* or with the consonant *g* followed by *e* or *y*.

   /j/ **j**eans, lar**ge**, **gy**m

► The starred word *judge* has two /j/ sounds in it. The first /j/ sound is spelled *j*, and the second is spelled *dge*.

► The /k/ sound can be spelled with *k*, *ck*, or *c*. The /kw/ sounds can be spelled with the *qu* pattern.

   /k/ par**k**, qui**ck**, pi**c**ni**c**   /kw/ s**qu**eeze

Write the Spelling Words that have the /j/ sound in them. Then write the Spelling Words that have the /k/ or /kw/ sounds in them.

Spelling Words

1. large
2. gym
3. skin
4. quick
5. picnic
6. judge
7. park
8. jeans
9. crack
10. orange
11. second
12. squeeze

/j/ Sound

_____

_____

_____

_____

_____

/k/ or /kw/ Sounds

_____

_____

_____

_____

_____

_____

Name _____

Spelling Spree

Silly Rhymes **Write a Spelling Word to complete each sentence. The answer rhymes with the underlined word.**

1. The hungry _____ ate some <u>fudge</u>.

2. Birds in the _____ sleep after <u>dark</u>.

3. I dropped baked <u>beans</u> on my new _____ .

4. There is a _____ in the train <u>track</u>.

5. Can more <u>bees</u> _____ into the hive?

6. A _____ <u>barge</u> is on the river.

1. large
2. gym
3. skin
4. quick
5. picnic
6. judge
7. park
8. jeans
9. crack
10. orange
11. second
12. squeeze

1. _____   4. _____

2. _____   5. _____

3. _____   6. _____

Letter Math **Solve each problem by using a Spelling Word.**

Example: joke – ke + b = *job*

7. pick – k + nic = _____

8. or + angel – l = _____

9. s + king – g = _____   11. sec + fond – f = _____

10. quit – t + ck = _____   12. edgy – ed + m = _____

Name _____

Proofreading and Writing

Proofreading Circle the five misspelled Spelling Words. Then write each word correctly.

1. large
2. gym
3. skin
4. quick
5. picnic
6. judge
7. park
8. jeans
9. crack
10. orange
11. second
12. squeeze

Dear Diary,

Today we went to the zoo. We saw larje snakes and turtles. One turtle splashed water on my geans! There was a dragon cage, but it was empty. I guess the dragons were taking a quik nap inside. For lunch we had a picnick. I ate mine in the parc.

1. _____

2. _____

3. _____

4. _____

5. _____

Write a List of Rules A baby dragon would need a lot of care. What rules should someone follow when raising a dragon?

On a separate sheet of paper, write a list of rules for taking care of a dragon. Use Spelling Words from the list.

Name _____

Say It Right!

Pronunciation Key							

ă	map	ĭ	pit	oi	**oil**	th	ba**th**
ā	pay	ī	ride	ŏŏ	b**oo**k	*th*	ba**th**e
â	care	î	**fi**erce	ōō	b**oo**t	ə	**a**go, it**e**m,
ä	father	ŏ	pot	ou	**out**		penc**i**l, at**o**m,
ě	pet	ō	go	ŭ	cup		circ**u**s
ē	be	ô	**paw**, **for**	û	fur		

Look at the vowel sound in the words below. Then look at the Pronunciation Key and find the sample word with the same vowel sound. Write the word on the line.

1. **must** (mŭst) _____ 8. **pair** (pâr) _____

2. **dirt** (dûrt) _____ 9. **meal** (mîl) _____

3. **breath** (brěth) _____ 10. **stay** (stā) _____

4. **path** (păth) _____

5. **chew** (chōō) _____

6. **self** (sělf) _____

7. **dear** (dîr) _____

Name _____

Looking for the Present

Read each sentence. Choose the correct verb form and write it on the line to complete the sentence.

1. This story _____ about a girl and her pet dragon. (tell   tells)

2. The dog _____ when it sees the giant egg. (barks   bark)

3. The neighbors _____ the egg hatching. (watch   watches)

4. A large claw _____ from inside the egg. (appear   appears)

5. The girl _____ the newborn dragon. (dry   dries)

6. The strange pet _____ when he sees the girl. (smiles   smile)

7. Her parents _____ about owning a dragon. (worries   worry)

8. Dragons _____ fire. (breathe   breathes)

9. The dragon _____ with the girl on his back. (flies fly)

10. Clouds _____ the two flying friends. (surround surrounds)

Name _____

Choosing the Present

Read each sentence. Then write the correct present-time form of the verb in parentheses.

1. A smart girl _____ a pet dragon. (raise)

2. The chickens _____ when they see the baby dragon. (cluck)

3. All animals _____ to eat. (need)

4. This dragon _____ on fish, frogs, eels, and insects. (munch)

5. The strange creature _____ to be a good friend. (try)

6. The friends _____ the farm together. (cross)

7. The dragon _____ with daily chores. (help)

8. His hot breath _____ the corn in the field. (pop)

9. Customers _____ the dragon's popcorn. (buy)

10. The girl _____ when the dragon leaves. (cry)

Name _____

Subject-Verb Agreement

**Proofread these paragraphs. Correct
errors in subject-verb agreement.
Circle verbs that are not in the correct time.
Then rewrite the paragraphs on the lines provided.**

Benjamin wakes at sunrise. He look outside his apartment
window. At first, he see only the sun. Then he spot five black dots
in the distance. The dots grows bigger and bigger. Suddenly, Ben's
jaw drop wide open. Five big black dragons flies outside his window.

The dragons calls to Benjamin. "Come fly with us!" they shout.
Benjamin think about it. In a few seconds, he decide. In a flash, he
jump onto one of the dragons. The new friends zooms into the air.
Benjamin laughs and wonder what will happen next.

_____

_____

_____

_____

_____

_____

_____

Name _____

Planning Your Writing

Use this page to plan your opinion. Then number your reasons or facts in the order you will use them.

Topic: _____

_____

_____

Topic Sentence/Opinion Statement: _____

_____

_____

Reason 1:	**Reason 2:**

Details that Explain Reason 1:	**Details that Explain Reason 2:**

Using Commas with Introductory Phrases

Select the introductory group of words from the box that best completes each sentence.

for example	first of all	in addition
in conclusion	most important	

Cats Are the Best Pets

I think cats are the best pets. (1)

_____ they are fun to watch.

(2) _____ if you roll a ball in

front of it, a cat will bat it around the house.

(3) _____ cats like to play with

string for hours. (4) _____ cats

are good companions. They follow you around the house,

and they sleep in your lap. (5) _____

those are the reasons why I think cats are the best pets!

Name _____

A Garden of Words

**Circle the word that best completes each sentence.
Then write the word in the blank.**

1. The elephants were so large they were _____ .
   A. impossible   C. awesome
   B. weak   D. smart

2. My teacher _____ me that some
   kinds of plants can eat insects.
   A. discovered   C. rewarded
   B. disappeared   D. convinced

3. I saw a bird in a tree, but it flew off and _____ .
   A. disappeared   C. grew
   B. discovered   D. walked

4. In the pond, I _____ a frog that
   looked like a leaf.
   A. thought   C. convinced
   B. discovered   D. read

5. We thought the lion's loud roar was _____ .
   A. quiet   C. incredible
   B. tiny   D. impossible

6. It was almost _____ to see

   the white polar bear sitting in the white snow.
   A. best   C. incredible
   B. awesome   D. impossible

Name _____

Story Map

The Garden of Abdul Gasazi

Characters	Setting

Plot

Problem

What Happens

Ending

Name _____

Mr. Gasazi's Garden!

Complete each sentence with an event from
The Garden of Abdul Gasazi. **Then explain how
you feel about the way the story ends.**

1. Miss Hester must visit Cousin Eunice, so she asks

_____

2. When Alan takes Fritz for a walk,

_____

3. As Alan searches for Fritz, he finds _____

4. The magician tells Alan that he has _____

_____

5. As Alan leaves, _____

6. When Alan returns to Miss Hester's, Fritz _____

_____

7. Miss Hester tells Alan that _____

8. After Alan leaves, Miss Hester tells Fritz that he is a bad dog

because _____

My Feelings About the Ending:

_____

_____

Name _____

The Shape of a Story

Read the story below.

Rescuing Dolly

One cold morning as Keisha walked her dog, Vista, she noticed fresh tracks in the snow. A minute later, a small, spotted dog appeared by the river. With no tag or collar, it clearly was lost. It stared hopefully at Keisha and shivered in the cold. Then Vista barked, and the dog ran off. "It's much too cold for a dog to stay outside for long," Keisha thought. "I've got to do something, but Vista will keep scaring it away."

So Keisha headed for home. She told her mother about the lost dog, and together they returned to the river to find it.

Keisha was almost ready to give up, but at last she spotted the dog. Keisha called to it, but it jumped onto a rock. Then Keisha knelt down. The little dog leaped into her arms and began licking her face.

Weeks later, the little dog's owner still could not be found. So that is how Dolly, the little dog, came to be part of Keisha's family.

Name _____

The Shape of a Story continued

Fill in this story map with details from "Rescuing Dolly."

Characters	Setting
1. _____	_____
2. _____	_____

Plot

Problem

_____

What Happens

1. _____

2. _____

3. _____

4. _____

Ending

1. _____

2. _____

Playing with Prefixes

On each line, write a word that begins with the
prefix *un-*, *dis-*, or *non-* and matches the definition.
Then find and circle all eight words in the word search.

1. not locked _____

2. not fiction _____

3. the opposite of agree _____

4. not able _____

5. the opposite of appear _____

6. not usual _____

7. not fair _____

8. not making sense _____

```
K N O N F I C T I O N D A D F P E P
D E R W H Y N E Z G Q J X H G H T V
I Z W U C Q X U S Y C Y S S V M Z C
S T V A N L N O N S E N S E Z P G Z
A N P K A L M B S U I G I V K A O R
P V N O W J O O D G S P H Q M H M Z
P T G J G Z O C R S S U N F A I R
E R Y X W L P F K X M P A Z H Z A R
A H E R J Q M W M E G V T L M O J E
R E U N A B L E L P D I S A G R E E
```

Name _____

Homophones

Homophones are words that sound the same but have different spellings and meanings. When you spell a homophone, think about the meaning of the word you want to write.

Homophone	Meaning
/noo/ **new**	not old
/noo/ **kn**ew	understood

Write the four pairs of Spelling Words that are homophones.

_____   _____

_____   _____

_____   _____

Now write the three Spelling Words that are homophones.

_____

_____

_____

Spelling Words

1. hear
2. here
3. new
4. knew
5. its
6. it's
7. our
8. hour
9. there
10. their
11. they're

Name _____

Spelling Spree

Quotation Caper Write the Spelling Word that best
completes each quotation that might have come
from the story.

1. "We magicians never reveal _____ secrets," said Mr. Gasazi.

2. "Your hat is not in _____ usual place," said Miss Hester.

3. "The ducks have flown back to _____ pond," said Alan.

4. "Fritz, come back _____ !" called Alan.

5. "Dogs should know that _____ not welcome here," grumbled Gasazi.

Spelling Words
1. hear
2. here
3. new
4. knew
5. its
6. it's
7. our
8. hour
9. there
10. their
11. they're

1. _____   4. _____

2. _____   5. _____

3. _____

In Another Word Write a Spelling Word
to replace each expression.

6. get wind of   _____

7. hot off the press   _____

8. over yonder   _____

9. got the picture   _____

Name _____

Proofreading and Writing

Proofreading Suppose that Alan keeps a journal.
Circle the five misspelled Spelling Words
in this entry. Then write each word correctly.

June 3: Today I had a strange adventure. It was in a
magician's garden. Miss Hester's dog Fritz ran in their.
I knue we were in trouble when I read the sign: "No dogs
allowed." I chased Fritz for at least an our. I think its'
possible that the magician turned Fritz into a duck!
When I came back heere, no one believed my story.

Spelling Words

1. hear
2. here
3. new
4. knew
5. its
6. it's
7. our
8. hour
9. there
10. their
11. they're

1. _____

2. _____

3. _____

4. _____

5. _____

Write a Plan Abdul Gasazi had some amazing trees
in his garden. If you could plan a garden, what would
you plant in it? Where would you plant things?

**On a separate sheet of paper, draw a picture of your
garden. Then write a plan for it. Tell what you
would plant, and where. Use Spelling Words from
the list.**

Name _____

Ask Your Friendly Thesaurus!

For each underlined word in the following sentences, choose a better word or words from the thesaurus entry. Write your answers in the blanks provided. Some words may have more than one answer.

Thesaurus Entries

1. **funny:** silly, unusual, curious, laughable
2. **pulled:** strained, dragged, stretched, heaved
3. **ran:** darted, flowed, fled, hurried
4. **tired:** exhausted, faint, worn, wilting
5. **walking:** strolling, trotting, striding, stomping
6. **shouted:** called, bellowed, howled, bawled

1. Fritz stopped chewing the furniture and fell asleep,

   completely tired. _____

2. Alan fastened Fritz's leash and the dog pulled him out of

   the house. _____

3. Fritz ran straight through the open door.

   _____

4. Gasazi shouted that he had turned the dogs into ducks!

   _____

5. Alan felt funny when he thought the magician had fooled

   him. _____

6. Fritz came walking up the front steps with Alan's hat.

   _____

196   Theme 3: **Incredible Stories**

Name _____

Choosing Time

Choose the correct verb form in parentheses and write it on the line provided to complete the sentence.

1. Tomorrow Alan _____ Fritz for a walk. (takes   will take)

2. Yesterday Alan _____ for Fritz. (searched   will search)

3. Yesterday in the garden, Fritz _____ into Abdul. (bumped   will bump)

4. Tomorrow Alan _____ the stairs. (climbed   will climb)

5. Yesterday the ducks _____ their wings. (flapped   will flap)

Complete the chart by supplying past and future time for each of the verbs given.

Verb	Past Time	Future Time
try	_____	_____
race	_____	_____
disappear	_____	_____
drag	_____	_____
bolt	_____	_____

Name _____

Writing Past and Future

Read each sentence. Then write the sentence in past time and future time.

1. Alan walks Fritz.

   Past: _____

   Future: _____

2. He hurries after the dog.

   Past: _____

   Future: _____

3. Alan discovers the magician.

   Past: _____

   Future: _____

4. Abdul shows Alan a duck.

   Past: _____

   Future: _____

5. The duck grabs Alan's hat.

   Past: _____

   Future: _____

Name _____

Keeping Verbs Consistent

Read this story. The paragraphs mix up the past, the present, and the future. The story takes place in the past. Circle any verbs that are not in past time. Then write the verbs correctly on the lines below.

I visited a strange garden yesterday. The bushes look like different animals. A giant green elephant watches the main path. I discovered a hidden path. I will follow the trail.

A strange noise sounds behind me. I turned around. The elephant moves! Then the giant plant faces in the other direction.

I decide to leave the weird garden. I try to find my way out. I looked everywhere. The paths twisted and turned.

I turn around again. The elephant watches me. I step farther into the garden. The elephant stared.

Finally, I uncover a hidden gate. I hurry toward it. The elephant appears in front of me. I raced out of the garden. Then I glance back. The garden is gone.

_____   _____   _____

_____   _____   _____

_____   _____   _____

_____   _____   _____

Theme 3: **Incredible Stories**   199

Name _____

Dialogue

Write the names of the characters and topic of the dialogue in the top box. Write what the characters say in the other boxes.

Characters' Names:
Topic:

Character:
Character's Words:

Character:
Character's Words:

Character:
Character's Words:

Character:
Character's Words:

Name _____

Write Quotations Right!

Rewrite each of the following sentences of dialogue that might have taken place. Add quotation marks, capital letters, or commas.

1. Miss Hester said please stay with Fritz and give him his afternoon walk.

_____

_____

2. don't chew on the furniture, Fritz Alan said angrily.

_____

_____

3. please, Fritz Alan exclaimed don't go running off into that garden!

_____

_____

4. Alan said if you have Fritz, Mr. Gasazi, would you please give him back?

_____

_____

5. something terrible has happened, Miss Hester Alan blurted out. your dog ran away, and Mr. Gasazi turned him into a duck!

_____

_____

Name _____

Writing a Personal Response

Use the test-taking strategies and tips you have learned to help you answer this kind of question. Take the time you need to decide which topic you will write about and to write an answer. Then read your response and see how you may make it better. This practice will help you when you take this kind of test.

Write one or two paragraphs about one of the following topics.

a. You have read *The Mysterious Giant of Barletta*. If you could choose a statue or something else to come to life, what would it be? Tell why you would choose it and how it might act.

b. Zia Concetta said *"grazie"* (thank you) to the Mysterious Giant. In what other ways do you think the townspeople could thank the Giant? How do you thank people for nice things they have done for you?

_____

_____

_____

_____

_____

_____

_____

_____

Name _____

Writing a Personal Response

continued

Read your answer. Check to be sure that it

- sticks to the topic.
- is well organized.
- has details that support your answer.
- has vivid and exact words.
- has few mistakes in capitalization, punctuation, grammar, or spelling.

Now pick one way you can improve your response.
Make your changes below.

_____

_____

_____

_____

_____

_____

_____

_____

_____

_____

_____

Name _____

Spelling Review

Write each Spelling Word. Then circle six words that are homophone pairs.

1. _____
2. _____
3. _____
4. _____
5. _____
6. _____
7. _____
8. _____
9. _____
10. _____
11. _____
12. _____
13. _____
14. _____
15. _____
16. _____
17. _____
18. _____
19. _____
20. _____
21. _____
22. _____
23. _____
24. _____
25. _____

Spelling Words

1. word
2. sound
3. clear
4. also
5. soft
6. crack
7. lawn
8. crown
9. girl
10. knew
11. here
12. turn
13. dark
14. north
15. orange
16. her
17. skin
18. hear
19. squeeze
20. gym
21. second
22. jeans
23. hour
24. our
25. new

Name _____

Spelling Spree

Puzzle Play Write a Spelling Word for each clue.
Then use the letters in the boxes to spell a word
about what a dragon is like.

1. this covers your body ☐ ___ ___ ___

2. first, —, third ___ ___ ☐ ___ ___ ___

3. heavy blue pants ___ ___ ☐ ___ ___

4. 60 minutes ___ ___ ☐ ___

5. a large indoor play area ___ ☐ ___

Secret Word: _____

Picture Clues Write Spelling
Words for each sentence.

6–7. The _____ is holding an

      _____ .

8–9. Stones from the _____ in

      the wall are lying on the _____ .

10–12. The king, wearing his _____ ,

       cannot _____ the soft

       _____ .

Name _____

Proofreading and Writing

**Proofreading Circle the five misspelled Spelling
Words below. Write each word correctly.**

It can be lonely hear in my big house. I don't
hear a werd from morning until darc. This morning,
however, I heard a saft sound. It was my friend
Masha, who held out a hand for me to skweeze.

1. _____   4. _____

2. _____   5. _____

3. _____

**Which Word? Write the Spelling Word that best fits
each group of words.**

6. understood or _____   11. opposite of south _____

7. unused or _____   12. boy and _____

8. in addition _____   13. to spin, circle, or _____

9. sunny and _____   14. we, us, _____

10. his or her _____

**Write Directions On another sheet of paper, write
directions telling the giant how to get from your
school to your house. Use the Spelling Review
Words.**

Spelling Words

1. clear
2. girl
3. turn
4. also
5. squeeze
6. dark
7. soft
8. north
9. her
10. new
11. here
12. our
13. knew
14. word

Student
Handbook

Contents

How to Study a Word

I. LOOK at the word.
► What does the word mean?
► What letters are in the word?
► Name and touch each letter.

2. SAY the word.
► Listen for the consonant sounds.
► Listen for the vowel sounds.

3. THINK about the word.
► How is each sound spelled?
► Close your eyes and picture the word.
► What familiar spelling patterns do you see?
► What other words have the same spelling patterns?

4. WRITE the word.
► Think about the sounds and the letters.
► Form the letters correctly.

5. CHECK the spelling.
► Did you spell the word the same way it is spelled in your word list?
► If you did not spell the word correctly, write the word again.

about	don't	I'd		
again	down	I'll		
almost		I'm	outside	tonight
a lot	enough	into		too
also	every	its	people	two
always	everybody	it's	pretty	
am				until
and	family	January	really	
another	favorite		right	very
anyone	February	knew		
anyway	field	know	said	want
around	finally		Saturday	was
	for	letter	school	Wednesday
beautiful	found	like	some	we're
because	friend	little	something	where
been	from	lose	started	while
before		lying	stopped	who
brought	getting		sure	whole
buy	girl	might	swimming	world
	goes	morning		would
cannot	going	mother	than	wouldn't
can't	guess	myself	that's	write
clothes			their	writing
coming	happily	never	them	
could	have	new	then	you
cousin	haven't	now	there	your
	heard		they	
does	her	off	thought	
didn't	here	one	through	
different	his	other	to	
done	how	our	today	

The Ballad of Mulan

More Short Vowels

/ŏ/ → l**o**t

/ŭ/ → r**u**b

Spelling Words

1. pond
2. luck
3. drop
4. lot
5. rub
6. does
7. drum
8. sock
9. hunt
10. crop
11. shut
12. won

Challenge Words

1. dodge
2. dusk

My Study List
Add your own spelling words on the back. ➡

Off to Adventure!
Reading-Writing Workshop

Look for familiar spelling patterns in these words to help you remember their spellings.

Spelling Words

1. have
2. haven't
3. found
4. around
5. one
6. than
7. then
8. them
9. before
10. because
11. other
12. mother

Challenge Words

1. family
2. cousin
3. everybody
4. guess

My Study List
Add your own spelling words on the back. ➡

The Lost and Found

Short Vowels

/ă/ → l**a**st

/ĕ/ → sm**e**ll

/ĭ/ → m**i**x

Spelling Words

1. mix
2. milk
3. smell
4. last
5. head
6. friend
7. class
8. left
9. thick
10. send
11. thin
12. stick

Challenge Words

1. empty
2. glance

My Study List
Add your own spelling words on the back. ➡

Take-Home Word List

Take-Home Word List

Take-Home Word List

Name _____

 My Study List

1. _____
2. _____
3. _____
4. _____
5. _____
6. _____
7. _____
8. _____
9. _____
10. _____

Review Words

1. test
2. dish

How to Study a Word

Look at the word.
Say the word.
Think about the word.
Write the word.
Check the spelling.

Name _____

 My Study List

1. _____
2. _____
3. _____
4. _____
5. _____
6. _____
7. _____
8. _____
9. _____
10. _____

How to Study a Word

Look at the word.
Say the word.
Think about the word.
Write the word.
Check the spelling.

Name _____

 My Study List

1. _____
2. _____
3. _____
4. _____
5. _____
6. _____
7. _____
8. _____
9. _____
10. _____

Review Words

1. hop
2. much

How to Study a Word

Look at the word.
Say the word.
Think about the word.
Write the word.
Check the spelling.

The Keeping Quilt

More Long Vowel Spellings

/ā/ → p**ai**nt, cl**ay**
/ē/ → l**ea**ve, f**ee**l

Spelling Words

1. paint
2. clay
3. feel
4. leave
5. neighbor
6. eight
7. seem
8. speak
9. paid
10. lay
11. need
12. weigh

Challenge Words

1. needle
2. crayon

My Study List
Add your own spelling words on the back. ➡

Off to Adventure!
Spelling Review

Spelling Words

1. last
2. mix
3. stick
4. lot
5. sock
6. hunt
7. wide
8. grade
9. thick
10. send
11. class
12. pond
13. luck
14. drum
15. save
16. cube
17. smile
18. left
19. smell
20. thin
21. drop
22. shut
23. huge
24. note
25. life

See the back for Challenge Words.

My Study List
Add your own spelling words on the back. ➡

The Waterfall

The Vowel-Consonant-*e* Pattern

/ā/ → s**a**v**e**
/ī/ → l**i**f**e**
/ō/ → sm**o**k**e**
/yōō/ → h**u**g**e**

Spelling Words

1. smoke
2. huge
3. save
4. life
5. wide
6. come
7. mine
8. grade
9. smile
10. note
11. cube
12. love

Challenge Words

1. escape
2. slope

My Study List
Add your own spelling words on the back. ➡

Take-Home Word List

Name _____

 My Study List

1. _____
2. _____
3. _____
4. _____
5. _____
6. _____
7. _____
8. _____
9. _____
10. _____

Review Words

1. side
2. hope

How to Study a Word

Look at the word.
Say the word.
Think about the word.
Write the word.
Check the spelling.

Take-Home Word List

Name _____

My Study List

1. _____
2. _____
3. _____
4. _____
5. _____
6. _____
7. _____
8. _____
9. _____
10. _____

Challenge Words

1. glance
2. empty
3. dusk
4. slope
5. escape

How to Study a Word

Look at the word.
Say the word.
Think about the word.
Write the word.
Check the spelling.

Take-Home Word List

Name _____

My Study List

1. _____
2. _____
3. _____
4. _____
5. _____
6. _____
7. _____
8. _____
9. _____
10. _____

Review Words

1. clean
2. play

How to Study a Word

Look at the word.
Say the word.
Think about the word.
Write the word.
Check the spelling.

The Talking Cloth

Three-Letter Clusters and Unexpected Consonant Patterns

spring
street
throw

/n/ ➔ **kn**ee
/r/ ➔ **wr**ap
/ch/ ➔ wa**tch**

Spelling Words

1. spring
2. knee
3. throw
4. patch
5. strong
6. wrap
7. three
8. watch
9. street
10. know
11. spread
12. write

Challenge Words

1. strength
2. kitchen

My Study List
Add your own spelling words on the back. ➔

217

Anthony Reynoso: Born to Rope

The Long *o* Sound

/ō/ ➔ c**oa**ch,
bl**ow**, h**o**ld

Spelling Words

1. coach
2. blow
3. float
4. hold
5. sew
6. though
7. sold
8. soap
9. row
10. own
11. both
12. most

Challenge Words

1. tomorrow
2. program

My Study List
Add your own spelling words on the back. ➔

217

Celebrating Traditions
Reading-Writing Workshop

Look for familiar spelling patterns in these words to help you remember their spellings.

Spelling Words

1. now
2. off
3. for
4. almost
5. also
6. can't
7. cannot
8. about
9. always
10. today
11. until
12. again

Challenge Words

1. February
2. January
3. Saturday
4. Wednesday

My Study List
Add your own spelling words on the back. ➔

217

Name _____

 My Study List

1. _____
2. _____
3. _____
4. _____
5. _____
6. _____
7. _____
8. _____
9. _____
10. _____

How to Study a Word

Look at the word.
Say the word.
Think about the word.
Write the word.
Check the spelling.

Name _____

 My Study List

1. _____
2. _____
3. _____
4. _____
5. _____
6. _____
7. _____
8. _____
9. _____
10. _____

Review Words

1. cold
2. slow

How to Study a Word

Look at the word.
Say the word.
Think about the word.
Write the word.
Check the spelling.

Name _____

My Study List

1. _____
2. _____
3. _____
4. _____
5. _____
6. _____
7. _____
8. _____
9. _____
10. _____

Review Words

1. catch
2. two

How to Study a Word

Look at the word.
Say the word.
Think about the word.
Write the word.
Check the spelling.

Dogzilla

The Vowel Sounds in *clown* and *lawn*

/ou/ ➡ cl**ow**n, s**ou**nd

/ô/ ➡ l**aw**n, cl**o**th, t**a**lk

Spelling Words

1. clown
2. lawn
3. talk
4. sound
5. cloth
6. would
7. also
8. mouth
9. crown
10. soft
11. count
12. law

Challenge Words

1. bounce
2. officer

My Study List
Add your own spelling words on the back. ➡

Celebrating Traditions
Spelling Review

Spelling Words

1. speak
2. feel
3. seem
4. most
5. both
6. know
7. street
8. lie
9. need
10. paint
11. hold
12. float
13. three
14. spread
15. mind
16. might
17. lay
18. leave
19. own
20. row
21. wrap
22. patch
23. tie
24. wild
25. bright

See the back for Challenge Words.

My Study List
Add your own spelling words on the back. ➡

Dancing Rainbows

The Long *i* Sound

/ī/ ➡ br**igh**t, w**i**ld, d**ie**

Spelling Words

1. wild
2. bright
3. die
4. sight
5. child
6. pie
7. fight
8. lie
9. tight
10. tie
11. might
12. mind

Challenge Words

1. design
2. delight

My Study List
Add your own spelling words on the back. ➡

Name _____

 My Study List

1. _____
2. _____
3. _____
4. _____
5. _____
6. _____
7. _____
8. _____
9. _____
10. _____

Review Words
1. find
2. high

How to Study a Word
Look at the word.
Say the word.
Think about the word.
Write the word.
Check the spelling.

Name _____

 My Study List

1. _____
2. _____
3. _____
4. _____
5. _____
6. _____
7. _____
8. _____
9. _____
10. _____

Challenge Words
1. needle
2. tomorrow
3. program
4. kitchen
5. design

How to Study a Word
Look at the word.
Say the word.
Think about the word.
Write the word.
Check the spelling.

Name _____

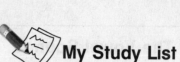 **My Study List**

1. _____
2. _____
3. _____
4. _____
5. _____
6. _____
7. _____
8. _____
9. _____
10. _____

Review Words
1. town
2. small

How to Study a Word
Look at the word.
Say the word.
Think about the word.
Write the word.
Check the spelling.

Raising Dragons

The /j/, /k/, and /kw/ Sounds

/j/ →	**j**eans, lar**ge**, **g**ym
/k/ →	par**k**, qui**ck**, pi**c**ni**c**
/kw/ →	**qu**ick

Spelling Words

1. large
2. gym
3. skin
4. quick
5. picnic
6. judge
7. park
8. jeans
9. crack
10. orange
11. second
12. squeeze

Challenge Words

1. courage
2. insect

My Study List
Add your own spelling words on the back. ➡

The Mysterious Giant of Barletta

Vowel + /r/ Sounds

/är/ →	d**ar**k
/î\r/ →	cl**ear**
/ôr/ →	n**or**th
/ûr/ →	h**er**, g**ir**l, t**ur**n, w**or**k

Spelling Words

1. girl
2. clear
3. her
4. turn
5. dark
6. work
7. smart
8. word
9. hurt
10. serve
11. north
12. third

Challenge Words

1. tornado
2. scurried

My Study List
Add your own spelling words on the back. ➡

Incredible Stories

Reading-Writing Workshop

Look for familiar spelling patterns in these words to help you remember their spellings.

Spelling Words

1. and
2. said
3. goes
4. going
5. some
6. something
7. you
8. your
9. friend
10. school
11. where
12. myself

Challenge Words

1. tonight
2. lying
3. field
4. enough

My Study List
Add your own spelling words on the back. ➡

Name _____

 My Study List

1. _____
2. _____
3. _____
4. _____
5. _____
6. _____
7. _____
8. _____
9. _____
10. _____

How to Study a Word

Look at the word.
Say the word.
Think about the word.
Write the word.
Check the spelling.

Name _____

 My Study List

1. _____
2. _____
3. _____
4. _____
5. _____
6. _____
7. _____
8. _____
9. _____
10. _____

Review Words

1. hard
2. morning

How to Study a Word

Look at the word.
Say the word.
Think about the word.
Write the word.
Check the spelling.

Name _____

 My Study List

1. _____
2. _____
3. _____
4. _____
5. _____
6. _____
7. _____
8. _____
9. _____
10. _____

Review Words

1. rock
2. job

How to Study a Word

Look at the word.
Say the word.
Think about the word.
Write the word.
Check the spelling.

Incredible Stories
Spelling Review

Spelling Words

1. sound	14. second
2. crown	15. here
3. word	16. new
4. her	17. soft
5. crack	18. turn
6. orange	19. north
7. hear	20. skin
8. our	21. gym
9. also	22. jeans
10. girl	23. hour
11. dark	24. knew
12. clear	25. lawn
13. squeeze	

See the back for Challenge Words

My Study List
Add your own spelling words on the back. ➡

The Garden of Abdul Gasazi

Homophones
Homophones are words that sound alike but have different spellings and meanings.

Spelling Words

1. hear
2. here
3. new
4. knew
5. its
6. it's
7. our
8. hour
9. there
10. their
11. they're

Challenge Words

1. seen
2. scene

My Study List
Add your own spelling words on the back. ➡

223 223

Take-Home Word List

Take-Home Word List

Name _____

 My Study List

1. _____
2. _____
3. _____
4. _____
5. _____
6. _____
7. _____
8. _____
9. _____
10. _____

Review Words

1. eye
2. I

How to Study a Word

Look at the word.
Say the word.
Think about the word.
Write the word.
Check the spelling.

Name _____

 My Study List

1. _____
2. _____
3. _____
4. _____
5. _____
6. _____
7. _____
8. _____
9. _____
10. _____

Challenge Words

1. officer
2. scurried
3. insect
4. seen
5. scene

How to Study a Word

Look at the word.
Say the word.
Think about the word.
Write the word.
Check the spelling.

Problem Words

Words	Rules	Examples
are our	*Are* is a verb. *Our* is a possessive pronoun.	<u>Are</u> these gloves yours? This is <u>our</u> car.
doesn't don't	Use *doesn't* with singular nouns, *he*, *she*, and *it*. Use *don't* with plural nouns, *I*, *you*, *we*, and *they*.	Dad <u>doesn't</u> swim. We <u>don't</u> swim.
good well	Use the adjective *good* to describe nouns. Use the adverb *well* to describe verbs.	The weather looks <u>good</u>. She sings <u>well</u>.
its it's	*Its* is a possessive pronoun. *It's* means "it is" (contraction).	The dog wagged <u>its</u> tail. <u>It's</u> cold today.
let leave	*Let* means "to allow." *Leave* means "to go away from" or "to let stay."	Please <u>let</u> me go swimming. I will <u>leave</u> soon. <u>Leave</u> it on my desk.
set sit	*Set* means "to put." *Sit* means "to rest or stay in one place."	<u>Set</u> the vase on the table. Please <u>sit</u> in this chair.
their there they're	*Their* means "belonging to them." *There* means "at or in that place." *They're* means "they are" (contraction).	<u>Their</u> coats are on the bed. Is Carlos <u>there</u>? <u>They're</u> going to the store.
two to too	*Two* is a number *To* means "toward." *Too* means "also" or "more than enough.	I bought <u>two</u> shirts. A cat ran <u>to</u> the tree. Can we go <u>too</u>? I ate <u>too</u> many peas.
your you're	*Your* is a possessive pronoun. *You're* means "you are" (contraction).	Are these <u>your</u> glasses? <u>You're</u> late again!

Read each question below. Then check your paper. Correct any mistakes you find. After you have corrected them, put a check mark in the box next to the question.

☐ 1. Did I indent each paragraph?

☐ 2. Does each sentence tell one complete thought?

☐ 3. Did I end each sentence with the correct end mark?

☐ 4. Did I begin each sentence with a capital letter?

☐ 5. Did I use capital letters correctly in other places?

☐ 6. Did I use commas correctly?

☐ 7. Did I spell all the words the right way?

Are there other problem areas you should watch for? Make your own proofreading checklist.

☐ _____

☐ _____

☐ _____

☐ _____

☐ _____

☐ _____

☐ _____

Mark	Explanation	Examples
¶	Begin a new paragraph. Indent the paragraph.	¶We went to an air show last Saturday. Eight jets flew across the sky in the shape of V's, X's, and diamonds.
∧	Add letters, words, or sentences.	The leaves were red ∧and orange.
℘	Take out words, sentences, and punctuation marks. Correct spelling.	The sky is bright blew. Huge clouds, move quickly.
/	Change a capital letter to a small letter.	The F̶ireflies blinked in the dark.
≡	Change a small letter to a capital letter.	New York city is exciting.

Writing Conference

In a writing conference, a writer reads a draft to a partner or a small group. The listeners tell what they like, ask questions, and make suggestions.

When you're the listener...

► Listen carefully as the writer reads.

► Say two things you like about the paper.

► Ask questions about anything you didn't understand.

► Share any ideas you have that might make the paper clearer or more interesting.

► Say your ideas in a way that will not make the writer feel bad.

When you're the writer...

► Read your paper aloud. Read slowly and clearly.

► Listen carefully to what your partner says.

► Take notes to remember any questions or suggestions.

► Afterwards, decide what changes you want to make in your paper.

What do I like about this paper?
How could it be better?

Guidelines for Writing a Friendly Letter

► Include the five parts of a friendly letter: heading, salutation (or greeting), body, closing, and signature.

► Indent the first line of the body and the first line of each new paragraph.

► Use informal language, as if you were talking to the person.

► Focus on one main idea in each paragraph. Tell events or other information in order.

► Include exact words and details that will interest your reader.

► End with a question or comments that encourage your reader to write back soon.

Writing Traits Rubric
Friendly Letter

**Use this rubric to evaluate your draft. Circle a number to
rate your writing, trait by trait. Then revise to improve your score.**

Writing Traits	Score 4	Score 3	Score 2	Score 1
✔ **Ideas** Did I include details that my reader will enjoy?	**4** I included plenty of details that my reader will enjoy.	**3** I included some details that my reader will enjoy.	**2** I included few details that my reader will enjoy.	**1** I included no details that my reader will enjoy.
✔ **Organization** Did I use all five parts of a letter?	**4** I used all five parts of a letter.	**3** I used most parts of a letter.	**2** I used some parts of a letter.	**1** I used few parts of a letter.
✔ **Sentence Fluency** Did I use a variety of different sentence types?	**4** There is great variety in my sentence types.	**3** There is some variety in my sentence types.	**2** There is little variety in my sentence types.	**1** There is no variety in my sentence types.
✔ **Word Choice** Did I use exact words and details?	**4** I used many exact words and details.	**3** I used some exact words and details.	**2** I used few exact words and details.	**1** I used no exact words or details.
✔ **Voice** Did I use an informal tone, as if I were talking to a friend?	**4** I used an informal tone throughout the letter.	**3** I used an informal tone in most of the letter.	**2** I used an informal tone in a few parts of the letter.	**1** I did not use an informal tone in the letter.
✔ **Conventions** Did I use correct spelling, grammar, and punctuation?	**4** There are no errors.	**3** There are few errors.	**2** There are some errors.	**1** There are many errors.

Guidelines for Writing a Personal Response Journal Entry

► Write down your thoughts and feelings about a selection you are reading.

► You can write what you think will happen next.

► You can write about anything that puzzles you.

► You can write about which characters you like and which you dislike, if any. You can also compare them to yourself or someone you know.

► You can write about how this story makes you feel or any memories it brings to mind.

► You can write ideas for projects that you thought of doing while reading the selection, such as a story that you might write.

► Write in any way you feel comfortable. Write sentences and paragraphs or list words and phrases.

► You can include drawings and photographs that relate to what you are reading.

Writing Traits Rubric
Journal Entry

Use this rubric to evaluate your draft. Circle a number to
rate your writing, trait by trait. Then revise to improve your score.

Writing Traits	Score 4	Score 3	Score 2	Score 1
✔ **Ideas** Did I record my thoughts and feelings about the selection?	**4** I recorded many thoughts and feelings about the selection.	**3** I recorded some thoughts and feelings about the selection.	**2** I recorded few thoughts and feelings about the selection.	**1** I recorded no thoughts or feelings about the selection.
✔ **Organization** Did I note the day of the week and the date?	**4** I noted the day of the week and the date.	**3** I noted the date only.	**2** I noted the day of the week only.	**1** I did not note the day of the week or the date.
✔ **Sentence Fluency** Did I avoid using sentence fragments in my writing?	**4** There are no sentence fragments in my writing.	**3** There is one sentence fragment in my writing.	**2** There are few sentence fragments in my writing.	**1** There are many sentence fragments in my writing.
✔ **Word Choice** Did I use descriptive details in my writing?	**4** I used plenty of descriptive details in my writing.	**3** I used some descriptive details in my writing.	**2** I used few descriptive details in my writing.	**1** I did not use descriptive details in my writing.
✔ **Voice** Does my interest in the topic show clearly?	**4** My interest in the topic shows very clearly.	**3** My interest in the topic shows somewhat clearly.	**2** My interest in the topic barely shows.	**1** My interest in the topic does not show.
✔ **Conventions** Did I use correct spelling, grammar, and punctuation?	**4** There are no errors.	**3** There are few errors.	**2** There are some errors.	**1** There are many errors.

232   Theme 1: **Off to Adventure!**

Guidelines for Writing a Paragraph That Explains

► Pick a topic you know well or would like to know about. You can explain why something happens or how something works.

► If you have chosen an unfamiliar topic, do any necessary research before you begin to draft.

► Begin with a topic sentence that tells what you will explain.

► Write supporting sentences that give facts or reasons that support your topic sentence.

► Organize supporting details in order of importance, from most important to least important, or in time order.

► Write a title that tells the topic and the main idea.

Writing Traits Rubric Explanation

Use this rubric to evaluate your draft. Circle a number to rate your writing, trait by trait. Then revise to improve your score.

Writing Traits	Score 4	Score 3	Score 2	Score 1
✔ **Ideas** Did I include a topic sentence and supporting sentences?	**4** I included a topic sentence and plenty of supporting sentences.	**3** I included a topic sentence and some supporting sentences.	**2** I included a topic sentence and few supporting sentences.	**1** I included a topic sentence but no supporting sentences.
✔ **Organization** Is the information in a logical order?	**4** All the information is in a logical order.	**3** Most of the information is in a logical order.	**2** Some of the information is in a logical order.	**1** None of the information is in a logical order.
✔ **Sentence Fluency** Did I vary my sentence types and lengths?	**4** There is excellent variety in my sentence types and lengths.	**3** There is good variety in my sentence types and lengths.	**2** There is little variety in my sentence types and lengths.	**1** There is no variety in my sentence types and lengths.
✔ **Word Choice** Did I clearly change my topic question into a topic statement?	**4** I clearly changed my topic question into a topic statement.	**3** I somewhat clearly changed my topic question into a topic statement.	**2** I changed my topic question into a topic statement.	**1** I did not change my topic question into a topic statement.
✔ **Voice** Did I use clear, simple language that my readers will understand?	**4** My language is very clear and simple.	**3** My language is mostly clear and simple.	**2** My language is somewhat clear and simple.	**1** My language is not clear and simple.
✔ **Conventions** Did I use correct spelling, grammar, and punctuation?	**4** There are no errors.	**3** There are few errors.	**2** There are some errors.	**1** There are many errors.

234   Theme 1: **Off to Adventure!**

Guidelines for Writing Paragraphs That Compare and Contrast

► Choose two subjects that are alike in some ways and different in others.
► Identify your subjects in the beginning.
► Think of details that explain how your subjects are alike.
► Think of details that explain how your subjects are different.
► Be specific. Use exact details and exact words.
► Organize details that tell how your subjects are alike into one paragraph.
► Organize details that tell how your subjects are different into another paragraph.
► Begin each paragraph with a topic sentence.

Writing Traits Rubric
Compare-Contrast Paragraph

Use this rubric to evaluate your draft. Circle a number to rate your writing, trait by trait. Then revise to improve your score.

Writing Traits	Score 4	Score 3	Score 2	Score 1
✔ **Ideas** Did I give examples of likenesses and differences?	**4** I gave several examples of likenesses and differences.	**3** I gave a couple of examples of likenesses and differences.	**2** I gave one example of a likeness and a difference.	**1** I gave no examples of likenesses and differences.
✔ **Organization** Did I start with a topic sentence and then group comparisons and contrasts?	**4** I started with a topic sentence and then grouped all comparisons and contrasts.	**3** I started with a topic sentence and then grouped most comparisons and contrasts.	**2** I started with a topic sentence but I mixed comparisons and contrasts together.	**1** I did not start with a topic sentence and I mixed the comparisons and contrasts together.
✔ **Sentence Fluency** Does my writing flow smoothly because I combined short sentences?	**4** I have very few short sentences. My writing flows very smoothly.	**3** I have some short sentences, but my writing still flows somewhat smoothly.	**2** I have several short sentences. My writing could flow more smoothly.	**1** I have too many short sentences. My writing does not flow smoothly.
✔ **Word Choice** Did I write strong descriptions to show how things are alike and different?	**4** I wrote many strong descriptions to show how things are alike and different.	**3** I wrote some strong descriptions to show how things are alike and different.	**2** I wrote few strong descriptions to show how things are alike and different.	**1** I wrote no strong descriptions to show how things are alike and different.
✔ **Voice** Is my writing clear and informative?	**4** My writing is very clear and informative.	**3** My writing is usually clear and informative.	**2** My writing is sometimes clear and informative.	**1** My writing is not clear and informative.
✔ **Conventions** Did I use correct spelling, grammar, and punctuation?	**4** There are no errors.	**3** There are few errors.	**2** There are some errors.	**1** There are many errors.

Guidelines for Writing on Demand

► Read the prompt, or question, carefully.

► Look for key words, or clues, in the prompt that tell you what to focus on. Are you summarizing? Are you expressing an opinion? Are you writing about a character?

► Be aware of how much time you have to answer the prompt. Divide the time. Plan time to quickly think about and organize your response. Plan time to write and edit your work.

► Before you write, think back to the passage or reread it. Keep the question in mind as you read.

► Make notes in an organized way. Draw a chart if you need to.

► Look at your notes. Which details or thoughts are most important? Be sure to include those first.

► Begin your answer or response by restating the question.

► As you write, use clear, exact language. Stay on the topic.

► When you finish, look back over your work and correct any mistakes.

Writing Traits Rubric Description

Use this rubric to evaluate your draft. Circle a number to rate your writing, trait by trait. Then revise to improve your score.

Writing Traits	Score 4	Score 3	Score 2	Score 1
✔ **Ideas** Did I include many interesting details?	4 I used plenty of interesting details.	3 I used some interesting details.	2 I used few interesting details.	1 I used no interesting details.
✔ **Organization** Did I answer all parts of the prompt?	4 I answered all parts of the prompt.	3 I answered some parts of the prompt.	2 I answered one part of the prompt.	1 I did not answer any parts of the prompt.
✔ **Sentence Fluency** Did I avoid writing run-on sentences?	4 There are no run-on sentences in my writing.	3 There are few run-on sentences in my writing.	2 There are some run-on sentences in my writing.	1 There are many run-on sentences in my writing.
✔ **Word Choice** Did I use key words from the prompt?	4 I used all the key words from the prompt.	3 I used some of the key words from the prompt.	2 I used one of the key words from the prompt.	1 I did not use any key words from the prompt.
✔ **Voice** Does my writing show my feelings?	4 Many details show my feelings.	3 Some details show my feelings.	2 Few details show my feelings.	1 No details show my feelings.
✔ **Conventions** Did I use correct spelling, grammar, and punctuation?	4 There are no errors.	3 There are few errors.	2 There are some errors.	1 There are many errors.

A Description

Prompt: The following article is about the Chinese Lion Dance. How do dancers and musicians give life to the lion? Write a description of the dancing lion. Use details of how the lion looks, what it does, and the sounds that go with it.

The Lion that Brings Luck

No Chinese New Year's celebration would be complete without a Lion Dance. Jumping, stretching, and turning inside the boldly colored lion costume are two dancers. One controls the head and front of the lion's body, while the other controls the back and the stubby tail. The dancers time their movements to the rhythmic sounds of a drum, cymbals, and a gong.

Lions of northern China are usually red, orange, or yellow. Southern lions come in many different colors. The front dancer can flutter the eyes, flap the mouth, and waggle the ears while twisting the head from side to side or up and down. The cloth body is sometimes trimmed with wavy lines. Often the dancers show their acrobatic ability by making the lion leap around on tall poles.

The Lion Dance probably originated two thousand years ago in China. A Chinese legend tells of a village terrorized by a fierce animal called a *nien*. The villagers dressed up in a lion costume and scared the *nien* away. That may be one reason why the lion is said to bring luck and why merchants leave "lucky money" for it on Chinese New Year's day.

Theme 2: **Celebrating Traditions**   239

Guidelines for Writing an Answer to a Question

► Read the question completely and carefully.
► Find the key words in the question that help you decide what the question is asking.
► Repeat the key words in your answer. You can rewrite the question as a statement to help focus your answer.
► Make sure you answer the question completely.
► Include facts and examples to support your answer.

Writing Traits Rubric
Answering a Question

Use this rubric to evaluate your draft. Circle a number to rate your writing, trait by trait. Then revise to improve your score.

Writing Traits	Score 4	Score 3	Score 2	Score 1
✔ **Ideas** Do my facts and examples provide the information asked for?	**4** My facts and examples provide all the information asked for.	**3** My facts and examples provide most of the information asked for.	**2** My facts and examples provide some of the information asked for.	**1** My facts and examples do not provide the information asked for.
✔ **Organization** Did I start with a topic sentence and follow it with facts and examples?	**4** I started with a topic sentence and followed it with several facts and examples.	**3** I put several facts and examples before the topic sentence.	**2** I did not write a topic sentence but I did provide facts and examples.	**1** I responded with a topic sentence only.
✔ **Sentence Fluency** Did I avoid sentence fragments?	**4** There are no sentence fragments in my writing.	**3** There are very few sentence fragments in my writing.	**2** There are some sentence fragments in my writing.	**1** There are many sentence fragments in my writing.
✔ **Word Choice** Does my response include key words from the question?	**4** My response includes all the key words from the question.	**3** My response includes some of the key words from the question.	**2** My response includes one key word from the question.	**1** My response includes none of the key words from the question.
✔ **Voice** Is my writing clear and informative?	**4** My writing is very clear and informative.	**3** My writing is usually clear and informative.	**2** My writing is sometimes clear and informative.	**1** My writing is not clear and informative.
✔ **Conventions** Did I use correct spelling, grammar, and punctuation?	**4** There are no errors.	**3** There are few errors.	**2** There are some errors.	**1** There are many errors.

Guidelines for Writing a Summary

► Use your own words.
► Make a story map to help you write the summary.
► For nonfiction, tell what the main idea is.
► For fiction, tell the main character's problem and the most important events.
► Describe the main events as briefly as possible.
► Tell the ending and how the main character feels about it.

Writing Traits Rubric
Writing a Summary

Use this rubric to evaluate your draft. Circle a number to rate your writing, trait by trait. Then revise to improve your score.

Writing Traits	Score 4	Score 3	Score 2	Score 1
✔ **Ideas** Did I include important ideas or events that will interest the audience?	**4** I included all the important ideas or events.	**3** I included almost all the important ideas or events.	**2** I included some important and some unimportant ideas or events.	**1** I included few important and many unimportant ideas or events.
✔ **Organization** Did I put main ideas and details in a logical order?	**4** All of the main ideas and details are in a logical order.	**3** Most of the main ideas and details are in a logical order.	**2** Some of the main ideas and details are in a logical order.	**1** The main ideas and details are not in a logical order.
✔ **Sentence Fluency** Did I vary my sentence lengths and types?	**4** There is excellent variety in my sentence lengths and types.	**3** There is good variety in my sentence lengths and types.	**2** There is some variety in my sentence lengths and types.	**1** There is little or no variety in my sentence lengths and types.
✔ **Word Choice** Did I use language that is a good fit for my audience?	**4** All of the language is a good fit for my audience.	**3** Most of the language is a good fit for my audience.	**2** Some of the language is a good fit for my audience.	**1** None of the language is a good fit for my audience.
✔ **Voice** Did I restate the author's ideas in my own words?	**4** Every sentence is in my own words.	**3** Almost every sentence is in my own words.	**2** I copied a few sentences.	**1** I copied many sentences.
✔ **Conventions** Did I use correct spelling, grammar, and punctuation?	**4** There are no errors.	**3** There are few errors.	**2** There are some errors.	**1** There are many errors.

Theme 2: **Celebrating Traditions**   243

Guidelines for Journal Writing

▶ Write in the first person. Use pronouns such as *I, me, my, mine, we* and *our.*

▶ Write about whatever interests you about your day.

▶ Explore thoughts and feelings about yourself and your world.

▶ Write in a way that feels natural. Choose words and phrases that sound like you.

▶ Don't worry about making mistakes. Journals are not finished products.

▶ Include drawings, lists, clippings, and other things that interest you.

▶ Try to write every day. Remember to date each entry.

Writing Traits Rubric
Journal Entry

Use this rubric to evaluate your draft. Circle a number to rate your writing, trait by trait. Then revise to improve your score.

Writing Traits	Score 4	Score 3	Score 2	Score 1
✔ **Ideas** Did I record the thoughts and feelings that were part of my experience?	**4** I recorded many thoughts and feelings that were part of my experience.	**3** I recorded some thoughts and feelings that were part of my experience.	**2** I recorded a few thoughts and feelings that were part of my experience.	**1** I recorded no thoughts and feelings that were part of my experience.
✔ **Organization** Did I include a date and put information in a logical order?	**4** I included a date and put all information in a logical order.	**3** I included a date and put most information in a logical order.	**2** I did not include a date but put some information in a logical order.	**1** I did not include a date and did not put information in a logical order.
✔ **Sentence Fluency** Did I vary my sentence types and lengths?	**4** There is excellent variety in my sentence types and lengths.	**3** There is good variety in my sentence types and lengths.	**2** There is little variety in my sentence types and lengths.	**1** There is no variety in my sentence types and lengths.
✔ **Word Choice** Did I include vivid, descriptive details?	**4** I included many descriptive details.	**3** I included some descriptive details.	**2** I included few descriptive details.	**1** I included no descriptive details.
✔ **Voice** Did I write in a voice that sounds casual and natural?	**4** All of my entry is in a casual, natural voice.	**3** Most of my entry is in a casual, natural voice.	**2** Some of my entry is in a casual, natural voice.	**1** None of my entry is in a casual, natural voice.
✔ **Conventions** Did I use correct spelling, grammar, and punctuation?	**4** There are no errors.	**3** There are few errors.	**2** There are some errors.	**1** There are many errors.

Theme 3: **Incredible Stories** 245

Guidelines for Writing a Thank-You Note

► Write the note as a letter or on the inside of a card.

► Name the gift or kind act at the beginning of the note.

► If you are writing about a gift, include details that show you have enjoyed it or noticed special features about it.

► If you are writing about a kind act, explain why the gesture meant something to you.

► Make the other person feel good about what he or she did.

► Remember to include all these parts of a letter: heading (address and date), greeting, body, closing, signature.

Writing Traits Rubric
Thank-You Note

Use this rubric to evaluate your draft. Circle a number to rate your writing, trait by trait. Then revise to improve your score.

Writing Traits	Score 4	Score 3	Score 2	Score 1
✔ **Ideas** Did I mention the kind act or gift and include details about it?	**4** I mentioned the kind act or gift and included many details about it.	**3** I mentioned the kind act or gift and included some details about it.	**2** I mentioned the kind act or gift and included few details about it.	**1** I mentioned the kind act or gift but included no details about it.
✔ **Organization** Did I include all five parts of a letter?	**4** I included all five parts of a letter.	**3** I included most parts of a letter.	**2** I included some parts of a letter.	**1** I included only the body of a letter.
✔ **Sentence Fluency** Did I vary the way my sentences start?	**4** There is much variety in the way my sentences start.	**3** There is some variety in the way my sentences start.	**2** There is little variety in the way my sentences start.	**1** There is no variety in the way my sentences start.
✔ **Word Choice** Did I use words that will make the reader feel good about what he or she did?	**4** I used many words that will make the reader feel good.	**3** I used some words that will make the reader feel good.	**2** I used few words that will make the reader feel good.	**1** I used no words that will make the reader feel good.
✔ **Voice** Is it clear that the kind act or gift was special to me?	**4** It's very clear that the kind act or gift was special to me.	**3** It's somewhat clear that the kind act or gift was special to me.	**2** It's a little hard to tell whether the kind act or gift was special to me.	**1** It's not clear at all that the kind act or gift was special to me.
✔ **Conventions** Did I use correct spelling, grammar, and punctuation?	**4** There are no errors.	**3** There are few errors.	**2** There are some errors.	**1** There are many errors.

Guidelines for Writing an Opinion Paragraph

► Begin with a topic sentence that clearly states your topic and your opinion about this topic.

► Provide at least three strong reasons that answer the question Why? about your opinion.

► Give details to explain each reason.

► Organize your reasons in order of importance. Tell your most important reason first or last.

► Restate your opinion and sum up your ideas in the conclusion.

Writing Traits Rubric
Opinion Paragraph

Use this rubric to evaluate your draft. Circle a number to rate your writing, trait by trait. Then revise to improve your score.

Writing Traits	Score 4	Score 3	Score 2	Score 1
✔ **Ideas** Are my opinion and the reasons for it clearly stated?	**4** My opinion and the reasons for it are very clear.	**3** My opinion and the reasons for it are mostly clear.	**2** My opinion and the reasons for it are somewhat clear.	**1** My opinion and the reasons for it are not clear.
✔ **Organization** Did I start with my opinion, follow it with reasons, and group details with the reasons they support?	**4** I started with my opinion, followed it with reasons, and grouped all details with the reasons they support.	**3** I started with my opinion, followed it with reasons, and grouped some details with the reasons they support.	**2** I started with my opinion, followed it with reasons, and mixed all details together.	**1** I used no logical order for my opinion, reasons, and details.
✔ **Sentence Fluency** Did I vary the way my sentences start?	**4** There is much variety in the way my sentences start.	**3** There is some variety in the way my sentences start.	**2** There is little variety in the way my sentences start.	**1** There is no variety in the way my sentences start.
✔ **Word Choice** Did I use exact nouns and verbs?	**4** I used many exact nouns and verbs.	**3** I used some exact nouns and verbs.	**2** I used few exact nouns and verbs.	**1** I used no exact nouns and verbs.
✔ **Voice** Is my personality strongly expressed in my opinion?	**4** My personality is strongly expressed in my opinion.	**3** My personality is somewhat expressed in my opinion.	**2** My personality is weakly expressed in my opinion.	**1** My personality is not expressed in my opinion.
✔ **Conventions** Did I use correct spelling, grammar, and punctuation?	**4** There are no errors.	**3** There are few errors.	**2** There are some errors.	**1** There are many errors.

Guidelines for Writing Dialogue

► Use dialogue to show a character's personality, or how a character thinks or feels: *"Of course,"* Sam smiled, *"I'd love to help."*

► Use dialogue to let characters tell story events: "Look out!" Christa yelled. "She's stealing second base!"

► Write dialogue that sounds like real people speaking.

► Avoid overusing the word *said*. Try using more exact words, such as *snapped*, *pleaded*, *shouted* and *asked*.

► Use correct capitalization and dialogue so that readers can easily follow what was said.

Writing Traits Rubric Dialogue

Use this rubric to evaluate your draft. Circle a number to rate your writing, trait by trait. Then revise to improve your score.

Writing Traits	Score 4	Score 3	Score 2	Score 1
✔ **Ideas** Are the characters' personalities obvious from my dialogue?	**4** The characters' personalities are very obvious from my dialogue.	**3** The characters' personalities are mostly obvious from my dialogue.	**2** The characters' personalities are somewhat obvious from my dialogue.	**1** The characters' personalities are not obvious from my dialogue.
✔ **Organization** Is it easy to figure out who is speaking in my dialogue?	**4** It is very easy to figure out who is speaking.	**3** It is somewhat easy to figure out who is speaking.	**2** It is a little hard to figure out who is speaking.	**1** It is hard to figure out who is speaking.
✔ **Sentence Fluency** Does my dialogue flow in a natural way?	**4** All of my dialogue flows in a natural way.	**3** Most of my dialogue flows in a natural way.	**2** Some of my dialogue flows in a natural way.	**1** None of my dialogue flows in a natural way.
✔ **Word Choice** Did I use vivid words to help show what my characters are like?	**4** I used many vivid words.	**3** I used some vivid words.	**2** I used few vivid words.	**1** I used no vivid words.
✔ **Voice** Does my dialogue sound like real people speaking?	**4** All of my dialogue sounds like real people speaking.	**3** Most of my dialogue sounds like real people speaking.	**2** Some of my dialogue sounds like real people speaking.	**1** None of my dialogue sounds like real people speaking.
✔ **Conventions** Did I use correct spelling, grammar, and punctuation?	**4** There are no errors.	**3** There are few errors.	**2** There are some errors.	**1** There are many errors.